Heroin

The Myths
and the Facts

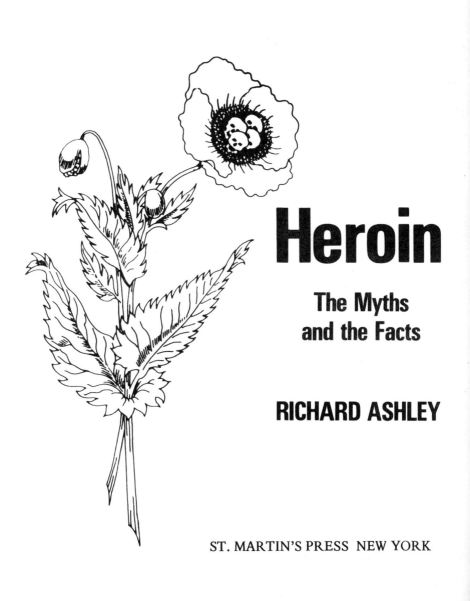

Heroin

The Myths and the Facts

RICHARD ASHLEY

ST. MARTIN'S PRESS NEW YORK

Library of Congress No. 72-89417
Manufactured in the United States of America.
No part of this book may be reproduced without
permission in writing from the publisher.

St. Martin's Press
175 Fifth Avenue
New York, N.Y. 10010

AFFILIATED PUBLISHERS:
Macmillan & Company, Limited, London
—also at Bombay, Calcutta, Madras and Melbourne—
the Macmillian Company of Canada, Limited, Toronto

Contents

Introduction vii

Heroisch: Large, Powerful 2

The Wonderful World of the BNDD 36

The Addict Personality 58

With Alice Through the Looking Glass 84

The Addict and the Law 108

The British Experience 144

Civil Commitment, Methadone, and
   Other Follies 170

The Search for a Solution 204

Appendices 227

Footnotes 253

Bibliography 265

Index 269

Introduction

When an oncoming car veers across the center-stripe, a threatened driver will react in microseconds. But no matter how sharp his reflexes, his reaction can never be simultaneous with the stimulus. There is always a time-lag. When an entire society is endangered, analogous mechanisms are set in motion. Unfortunately they are never as efficient as our personal survival instincts. The stimuli are more diverse, the reactions often contrary and diffuse, and the time-lag is enormous—years instead of microseconds. And unlike a car on the wrong side of the road, no great social problem is ever so direct and simple as to allow an immediate and satisfying solution. Even if, for example, we manage to end the fighting in Vietnam, we still must deal with the products of the war—not the least of which is the coming home of many thousands of young men addicted to heroin.

Time-lag can never be eliminated, but it can be reduced. It need not have taken a century after a civil war to enact civil rights legislation. It need not have taken decades after the dangers were recognized to start acting to reduce pollution. Nor should it take years to do something about heroin.

But no major social action occurs in this country unless the government feels it has the support of the voters, and this support is rarely evident, except when the majority of voters are directly threatened by a situation. And, until quite recently, those best able to move the government to action, the white middle class, did not feel threatened by heroin. Of course, some of the side effects of heroin addiction—muggings and robberies, crime in the streets—*did* affect the white middle class. Their chief responses were cries for more police protection and, for those who could afford it, a hasty move to the suburbs. They feared assaults on their persons and property. Now in the 1970s they have something more to fear, and this is being reflected in the current intense concentration on the heroin problem by the media, legislators, police officials and the medical profession. It is a fear triggered by a far more immediate threat than the off-chance of being mugged: heroin is no longer confined to the ghettos; it has moved into the white man's turf. Kids are dying of overdoses (o.d.'s) in Westchester County.

It was the recognition of this new danger which caused the Nixon Administration to quietly shut down Operation Intercept, the much-touted drive to cut the flow of marijuana into the country. Intent on showing its willingness and ability to act against illicit drug usage, the Administration moved vigorously against the drug the country had heard most about, a mild euphoric whose widespread use by young people disturbed their elders. A good political move, it seemed . . . until it backfired. In the fiscal year ending June 30, 1971, the Bureau of Customs seized 973 pounds of heroin. In the fiscal year ending June 30, 1970 (the year of Operation Intercept), only forty-six pounds were taken.[1] A great increase in heroin traffic did not account for this remarkable difference. The cause was much simpler: most of the Feds were down on the Mexican border looking for marijuana. To parents in the process of discovering that their children could now buy heroin in Scarsdale and Grosse Pointe, these figures might be hard to explain. No matter how uninformed, they were not likely to believe that marijuana was as dangerous as heroin. Operation Intercept ended less than a year after it began.

The government's realization that heroin had moved

out of the ghetto came at least two years after the fact and a good three years after the youth drug culture had radically changed. And there is little evidence to indicate they are yet aware of the dimensions of this change. From the current flow of federally-financed pamphlets and films on the subject, one would suppose that among the more potent drugs, LSD is the most widely used. Yet anyone familiar with the drug scene knows that good LSD is very hard to come by and has been since 1969. The big market these days is in downers ("downs" as opposed to "ups"— barbiturates and tranquilizers as opposed to amphetamines) and heroin. Drugs are like any other commodity: supply flows to meet demand. And LSD is not in demand.

There are reasons for this change. Heroin is popular because it turns the user off, makes him indifferent to his surroundings. Marijuana was never that big in the black ghettos—who wants to be turned on and sensitized to rats and cockroaches? LSD was popular when the young still believed their life-style and actions would change the country for the better. After years of fruitless marching to end the war, years of political frustration and years of inflation and recession, this belief subsided. And with it the prevalence of psychedelics.

Ignorance and the inertia of bureaucracy will make it difficult to treat the symptoms of the heroin disease, let alone do anything about its root causes. In 1971 the government was still churning out great reams of material on the dangers of marijuana and LSD, while at the same time telling us that there were "100,000 to 200,000 heroin addicts in the country" (A Federal Source Book: *Answers to the Most Frequently Asked Questions About Drug Abuse*, Revised, June 1971), when the actual figure was probably close to 750,000. It wasn't until 1972 that federal officials began showing some realism in their estimates of the heroin-using population. The Bureau of Narcotics and Dangerous Drugs came up with a figure of 315,000,[2] and a month or so later, Myles Ambrose, who had been appointed to head up President Nixon's new "war on drugs," allowed that there were as many as 560,000 users in the country.[3] Mr. Ambrose, however, was of the opinion that most of these were of very recent origin, an opinion not consistent with the facts and one which left the impression that the new figure was more a device to pry money from the Congress than an admission that the drug bureaucracy had for years seriously under-estimated the problem. It is hard to do much about a problem when you are not aware of its dimensions. Hopefully, what follows will acquaint you with those dimensions.

And yes, while reading about heroin, don't make the mistake of believing it to be the awful excrescence of some alien drug culture, something that perhaps, God forbid, might even reach your own children if the police don't do something about those pushers. America doesn't *have* a drug culture, America *is* a drug culture. A drug culture, moreover, heavily dependent on central nervous system depressants — downers — of which heroin is simply the strongest. Alcohol is socially acceptable, but we have 9,000,000 alcoholics, and alcohol is a downer. Billions of barbiturate and tranquilizer doses are sold each year. And every hour of the day in every major city in America you can hear the line "For headache take aspirin—for nervous tension take Compoz." The country is inundated with such advertising. If alcohol and Compoz don't do it for you, your friendly family doctor will prescribe Valium or Librium. Not every doctor can be persuaded to prescribe Percodan, but there's no harm in trying. And if things really get hard and you are no longer able to take it or face it, the heaviest of downers is readily available from your friendly neighborhood dealer. Are you ready for smack?

Heroisch: **Large, Powerful**

If archeology and history are any indicators, we have from the beginning felt a great need for substances which would either expand or depress our consciousness. At no point do we appear to have been entirely satisfied with our day-to-day existence. For since mankind began banding together in settlements larger than the cave, there is ample evidence of drug usage. From the earliest recorded times, the range has been wide: from the relative mildness of beer and marijuana to the power of opium and the psychedelic mushroom.

As technology and population advanced, life became more complex, more fraught with tension and anxiety—and for many, less and less satisfying. It is not surprising then that the present age uses both the most powerful of psychedelics, LSD-25, and the most powerful of central nervous system depressants, heroin.

Heroin did not spring fully-formed from the brow of Zeus. It is derived from morphine, and morphine from opium. Without opium there can be no heroin, and the effects of opium—the dulling of pain, detachment from the anxieties of existence, and euphoria—have been known from at least the third millennium B.C. To the Sumerians of that period, the opium poppy, the *Papaver somniferum,* was known as the joy-plant. Homer called it nepenthe, that "potent destroyer of grief." He attributed its discovery to the Egyptians, and there is clear evidence they used the drug medicinally, but whether they discovered its effects themselves or learned its use from the inhabitants of Asia Minor, where the opium poppy was first cultivated is not known. At any rate, the use of opium spread to Greece and then to Rome. The first extensive account of its pharmacology appears in the writings of Theophrastus in the third century B.C., and Pliny was thoroughly familiar with its effects. And it can be assumed that opium addiction was a not uncommon phenomenon in the ancient world. The third century B.C. Greek physician Erasistratus recommended complete avoidance of the drug because of its addictive nature.[1]

Archeological evidence reveals that virtually all the peoples of the Near and Middle East—from the Babylonians to the Hebrews—were familiar with opium both as a pain-killer and a producer of euphoria. Alexander the Great took opium to India in the fourth century B.C., but there is no evidence that it was used or known by the Indians of the period. Their introduction to opium apparently occurred much later via Persia and Arabia.[2]

Opium made its first appearance in China during the early part of the seventh century A.D., carried there by Arab traders.[3] Until the middle of the seventeenth century, it seems to have been used only medicinally, chiefly as a cure for dysentery. Then in 1620 the use of tobacco reached China from the Philippines. Shortly after this time, the Dutch in Formosa discovered that a combination of tobacco and opium when smoked seemed helpful in preventing malaria. This practice spread to Fukien on the neighboring mainland and by the end of the seventeenth century opium was being smoked with no thought of suppressing dysentery or preventing malaria. Some 2,700 years after the Greeks, the Chinese had discovered that opium alleviated other than bodily pains.

Smoking opium for pleasure spread very rapidly, and its evils were evident enough by 1729 that the Emperor Yung Cheng issued a decree prohibiting the opening of smoking dens and the sale of opium for smoking. The decree had little effect. At the time the Chinese opium trade was controlled by the Portuguese, and during the first year of the prohibition, they brought in 200 chests of Indian opium, each containing 133 1/3 pounds. The quantity of imported Indian opium gradually increased, and by 1790 the annual amount had risen to 5,000 chests. In 1800 the Emperor Chia Ch'ing issued a new decree banning the cultivation of the opium poppy in China and the importation of opium from abroad. Once again the decree had little effect. The foreign traders, particularly the English East India Company, which from 1773 had largely controlled the trade, were making too much money to worry about legal niceties—as were the Chinese officials who worked with them. During the last six years of the company's monopoly, 1828-1834, 92,957 chests of opium—approximately 1,000 tons per year—were shipped into China, at a value which amounted to fifty-four percent of all the exports carried on the annual balance sheets of the company. After the company's monopoly was ended, the British free traders, along with the American, Dutch, French, and Portuguese pushed the opium trade with the energy usually evident only when great profits are to be made. During a one-year period, 1838-1839, an estimated 40,000 chests (2,670 tons) made their way into China. (In contrast, my calculations indicate that thirty-three tons of heroin enter the United States each year.)

Feeling that the problem had gotten out of hand, the Chinese government decided to strictly enforce the opium laws. The only results of their decision were the Opium Wars of 1839-1842, which they lost; the serious reduction of Chinese sovereignty; and a marked increase in the opium trade. By 1858, 5,000 tons were coming in each year. By 1906 only 3,500 tons were being imported, but the Chinese were producing 10,000 tons a year themselves. Some historians estimate that by this time fifty percent of the adult male population were addicted to opium.

Meanwhile, the medicinal use of opium in the West was

also growing. In the early part of the sixteenth century the physician Paracelsus compounded a hydroalcoholic tincture containing ten percent opium. Called laudanum, it became a standard drug for the suppression of coughing and diarrhea, and was the most common of sedatives up through the nineteenth century. No prescription was required, and since its addictive qualities were not clearly understood, a great many people became unwitting addicts—Coleridge, De Quincey, Swinburne and Edgar Allan Poe among them. In 1814 the American physician, Dr. Barton, concoted the "brown mixture"—opium and licorice. It too became a staple remedy. Then followed a wide variety of patent medicines based on opium, and by the end of the nineteenth century, it was estimated that anywhere from one in 400 to one in 20 Americans were addicted to opium, chiefly through the use of patent medicines.[4] (Today, depending on which estimates you consult, one in every 2,000, one in every 1,000, one in every 500, or one in every 210 Americans is addicted to heroin.)

Morphine, a natural alkaloid of opium and the next step on the ladder from opium to heroin, was first isolated in 1803. Its superior pain-reducing qualities quickly gained it high repute with the medical profession. In this country it was first widely used during the Civil War, so widely and freely used, in fact, that by the end of the war some 45,000 soldiers were addicted to morphine.[5] This particular addiction became known as the soldier's disease. Medicine faced a perplexing problem. It had in morphine the best pain-killer yet devised, and in both opium and morphine, drugs which were efficacious for a wide variety of common ailments. They were fine cough suppressants, good remedies for diarrhea and dandy relievers of minor aches. The trouble was that they often led to an illness far

5

more serious than that for which they were prescribed. The good drugs were producing addicts.

Then in 1898 the Bayer Company of Germany, anxious to find a drug which could do the work of morphine without incurring the liabilities of morphine use, created a semisynthetic derivative of morphine, which they named heroin (from the German *heroisch:* large, powerful). Heroin was indeed large and powerful. Two or three times as potent a pain-killer as morphine, it was also soon found capable of relieving morphine withdrawal symptoms. Despite these powers, heroin was considered nonaddictive. A new miracle drug was in the medicine chest.

There was also a new drug in the addict's chest. For though it took twelve years for the doctors to discover that heroin was at least as addictive as morphine, drug users apparently learned so even earlier. The word "junk" was already an established slang term for heroin in the very early 1900s. Heroin soon replaced morphine and opium as the drug of choice among opiate addicts, for though very similar in effect to morphine when taken in equipotent doses, it also provides greater euphoria and stimulation. Moreover, it is less bulky than morphine: one-half the bulk even after morphine is reduced to a soluble powder form. Thus, in a smaller, easier-to-secrete package, you have a more potent and more appealing product ... and a more profitable one.

By 1924 Congress, responding to administrative and court interpretations of the Harrison Narcotics Act of 1914, had prohibited the manufacture of heroin in the United States, and in 1956 all existing stocks on hand in pharmacies and pharmacological laboratories were required to be surrendered or destroyed.[6] These actions had no discernible effect on the illicit market. Heroin is being produced in quantities great enough and delivered in a manner efficient enough that, according to narcotics agents in New York, there has not been a serious shortage in the city since 1967.[7] When occasional mild panics do occur, they are usually the result of dock strikes. If the longshoremen walk out, there is no way to get the stuff off the boats.

Of course no one would have to worry about dock strikes if heroin were manufactured here—and some have wondered why it isn't. After all, this country has long been noted for ingenious and enterprising types quite willing to supply any market for the proper price. The trouble is that though several parts of the country are suitable for the cultivation of the opium poppy (in the nineteenth century, opium poppies were grown and harvested in California, Arizona, Florida, Louisiana, Vermont, Connecticut, and New Hampshire.),[8] it would not, on the scale required, be at all easy to do so undetected. And even if this were somehow possible, the collection of crude opium from which morphine base and then heroin is made, is a slow and tedious process, economically feasible only in areas where labor costs are very low.

This is the method: A few days after the petals have fallen from the flower, the seed pods are delicately incised in several places. Droplets of a milklike substance ooze forth. They are left to dry on the surface of the pod. The next day the dried droplets, now brown and having a gummy consistency—crude opium—are scraped off and collected into lumps. A good worker needs about a day to gather a kilo. With crude opium selling at $25 a kilo, one can readily see that cultivating the opium poppy in the United States would not be a money-making proposition even at the wages paid a migrant farm worker.

Since the United States manufactures no heroin, the

heroin used here must be smuggled in from abroad. It is generally agreed, but open to question, that Turkey still, as of 1972, supplies the opium from which most of the heroin for the American market is made. The next largest primary source is Southeast Asia. Some heroin for our market is made from Mexican opium, but no one seems to think Mexico will become a major supplier in the near future, if only because Mexico is simply not geared to compete in opium production with either Turkey or Southeast Asia.

Southeast Asia, particularly in the area known as the Golden Triangle, where Thailand, Laos and Burma meet, probably produces more opium that the rest of the world combined. Little of this production is subject to government control. Respecting this region, the United Nation's International Narcotics Control Board has said that " . . . There can be little doubt that . . . the quantities [of opium] entering the illicit traffic . . . exceed the total [world] licit production." (In 1969 the world's reported licit production was 1,219 tons.)[9] Only a part of the Golden Triangle's opium production is being made into heroin, since the major drug market in Southeast Asia is still opium. But this is beginning to change. The Board's July-September 1971 Bulletin on Narcotics states that " . . . the traditional consumption of opium in Thailand was widely given place to heroin addiction."[10] Heroin flows out of the Golden Triangle along the traditional drug routes of the opium trade, to Bangkok, Singapore, Hong Kong, and Tokyo. Until the spring of 1970 very little of this heroin reached the American market in Vietnam. Then the Chinese, who control the opium and heroin traffic in the area, found that there was a demand for heroin among the G.I.s. They set up a half-dozen refineries (a heroin refinery can fit in a couple of large bathrooms) in the mountains and began producing a heroin specifically designed for the G.I. market. This heroin, H-4, is forty to fifty percent pure (as compared to the seven to ten percent junk usually sold in Harlem). Within six months they had created a major market and a major problem for the Army.[11] There is evidence that fifty kilos a week of H-4 are brought into Saigon.[12] In New York one kilo cut to seven to ten percent heroin will provide the daily needs for approximately 6,000 addicts with six-bags-a-day habits. Seven kilos a week takes care of 6,000 New York junkies. What does fifty "keys" of forty to fifty percent H-4 do in Saigon?

The government claims that less than six percent of the troops show signs of heroin use, but experienced reporters in Vietnam and other observers find this figure ludicrously low. The government based its estimate on urine tests given 86,082 soldiers in Vietnam between June 18, 1971, and September 10, 1971. The tests reportedly indicated that "only" 5.5 percent showed positive signs of opiate use, some of which was very likely opium use rather than heroin use.[13] They didn't bother to inform the American public that "almost every man tested knew exactly what day he would be tested and that he could escape detection by abstaining from heroin for twenty-four to seventy-two hours prior to the tests."[14] Moreover, a black market in "clean" urine quickly developed.[15] At best then, the 5.5 percent figure represented hard-core addicts unable to either abstain for the required time or to buy "clean" urine samples. Congressmen Morgan Murphy of Illinois and Robert Steele of Connecticut toured Southeast Asia in April of 1971 and reported that ten to fifteen percent of the American troops were using heroin at the time. They said that in some units heroin addiction had "crippled from fifteen to forty percent" of the troops.[16] In short, the most objective estimates held that 30 to 40,000 American G.I.s were using heroin in Vietnam during 1971.[17] The Nixon Administration has taken care of this problem by shipping most of our troops home, including thousands of junkies, the great majority of whom have received little or no treatment for their addiction. (See Appendix C)

How much of this Asian heroin is reaching the United States? John B. Williams in his book *Narcotics* (1963), says, "The major source of the international illicit narcotics traffic has been and still is Communist China." Williams based this statement on information from Harry Anslinger, who was quite sure the Chinese Communists were bent on destroying us with heroin.[18] It was testimony suited to please the China Lobby and other Cold War stalwarts, but so far as it can be ascertained, there wasn't then, nor is there now, a shred of evidence showing this this to be true. Indeed, all available evidence is to the contrary. Chinese *are* highly involved in the Southeast Asia drug traffic. They supply the traditional markets and the American soldiers. But few of these Chinese are Chinese Communists. The group who control the business are often called the Chinese Mafia, immigrants from the coastal area of Chu Chow who moved into Vietnam, Laos, Cambodia, Thailand, and Burma and organized the opium trade. There is also Nationalist Chinese involvement, notably the 93rd Division of the old Nationalist Army, which has made its living by patrolling the opium caravan routes in Burma, Thailand, and Laos.[19] The drug merchants pay them for safe passage. Some of this heroin reaches the American mainland. No one knows precisely how much, but certainly more comes in than is admitted by American officials.

This reluctance to admit the extent of the Southeast

Asia traffic to the United States is understandable, if not laudable. For almost a decade it has been an article of faith among our drug bureaucrats that eighty percent of our illicit heroin originates in Turkish opium: "As much as eighty percent of the heroin flowing to United States users comes from fields in Turkey," said John E. Ingersoll, Director of the Bureau of Narcotics and Dangerous Drugs, in testimony before the Select House Committee on Crime in August 1969.[20] Mr. Ingersoll so testified, even though he could hardly have been unaware that the United Nations Commission on Narcotic Drugs had, in its 1966 *Report of the 21st Session,* clearly demonstrated that the leakage of licit opium, most of which occurred with Middle East producers and especially Turkey, "was only fractional and . . . the illicit traffic did not depend for the bulk of its supplies on quantities diverted from licit production." The report went on to state that the illicit production in Southeast Asia, the great bulk of which is in the Golden Triangle area, " . . . constituted 80% of all illicit supplies as at present estimated."[21]

Oddly enough, the BNDD's insistence that Turkey is the mother lode of illicit heroin is of fairly recent origin. Through the 1950s the Bureau stoutly maintained that most of our heroin originated in Communist China. Indeed up until 1964 the United States continually complained to the United Nations that heroin from the Chinese mainland was being smuggled here as part of the Red Chinese "twenty-year plan to finance political activities and spread addiction."[22] And as late as 1960 the United States was claiming that "the principal sources of diacetylmorphine [heroin] seized in the United States were Hong Kong, Mexico and Communist China."[23]

The U.N.'s Commission on Narcotic Drugs set the record straight. They noted that there was no evidence

11

that Communist China was exporting opiates and that the Hong Kong heroin came via Thailand, not the Chinese mainland. They also noted that the "999" brand of morphine the Bureau insisted on calling "Red Chinese" was in fact delivered by Nationalist Chinese troops from stocks in Burma and northern Thailand. They further noted the presence of

> remnants of KMT troops [Kuomintang (Nationalist Chinese) troops], who were maintaining themselves largely on the profits of the opium trade. It was reported that they received their supplies periodically by air.[24]

The air supplier was CAT, a Nationalist Chinese airline funded by the United States.

When U.S. involvement in Vietnam intensified in 1965, the references to the main supplier of heroin being Southeast Asia suddenly stopped. Coincidentally, Turkey was identified as the chief supplier, and our efforts to halt the international heroin traffic were centered on the Middle East.

The reason? Perhaps Turkey had become the chief supplier or perhaps the well-documented fact that high government officials in Vietnam, Thailand, Laos, and Cambodia were heavily implicated in the opium, morphine, and heroin traffic had something to do with it. We support these governments and provide them with enormous amounts of material and money to help further our policies in Southeast Asia. And though some of this money is used to finance the opiate trade, our government's policy is apparently one of not rocking the boat, whatever the costs—to the extent, indeed, that American personnel, including Green Berets and the C.I.A., have been, and possibly still are, directly involved in this trade.

> United States Special Forces, or Green Berets, and the C.I.A., were up to here in the traffic—for, to be sure,

political reasons. Green Berets were ordered to buy certain supplies of opium in order to make and maintain staunch allies among the growers cum guerrillas.[25]

And

Large-scale traffickers such as the Kuomintang . . . were given the use of C.I.A. planes. Even when the Kuomintang hit upon the scheme of processing its own opium [they had hitherto confined themselves to transporting opium] to increase profits, U.S. officials did nothing, although the C.I.A. could not have failed to notice refineries in the area of the "fertile triangle," refineries which turned out ninety-six percent pure heroin.[26]

That the U.S. Government has been knowingly involved in the illicit heroin trade has been documented in a number of articles and books, giving explicit details as to locations, persons involved and manner of operation.[27] And most recently the Senate's Foreign Operations Appropriations Subcommittee heard testimony to the effect that "South Vietnam's heroin racket is run by three of that nation's top politicians, is linked to Corsican and U.S. Mafia gangsters and is virtually condoned by some U.S. officials."[28] Also, that "top military leaders in Laos, Cambodia and Thailand are heavily involved in the drug trade,"[29] as well as elements of the Vietnamese Air Force. Those implicated were, among others, President Thieu, former President Ky, Prime Minister Tran van Khiem of Vietnam and General Ouane Rattikone, former Chief of Staff of the Royal Laotian Army. The testimony noted that "overwhelming evidence of systematic corruption" extended all the way to the top of the Saigon government and that some of Thieu's closest allies inside the Vietnamese Army "control the distribution and sale of heroin to American G.I.s fighting in Indochina."[30]

In response to Nixon's "war on drugs," some action was taken in Southeast Asia in late 1971: "The C.I.A. and

13

other agencies bought off certain dealers (including a general, who was paid to retire) who had been their friends and who were deeply involved in opium." A few raids were staged to show that we meant business, and a few refineries were shut down. As a result, the refineries were moved to Burma and Thailand, where there now exists "the highest concentration of refineries in the world . . . Marseilles cannot compare."[31]

The 30 to 40,000 American heroin users in Vietnam were customers of these American-aided dope rings, and this same dope is now flowing into the United States. Has this been official American policy? Well, certainly some American officials must have condoned it, otherwise the C.I.A. and Green Berets could not have been involved as they were, nor could high officials in the governments we support have operated untouched. It wasn't condoned because Johnson and Nixon were eager to see more dope in America and more addicts in the American Army; it was simply that the United States Government's chief concern has been the war in Indochina, and this has involved keeping the loyalty of the local regimes it supports or, more to the point, the loyalty of high officials in these regimes. And " . . . if this meant the continued production of opium in the sensitive areas . . . this was all right with the U.S."[32]

Although there has been a great deal of evidence, enough anyway to convince seasoned reporters and United Nations investigators of U.S. involvement in the Southeast Asia heroin traffic—e.g., Dr. Joel Fort, who studied the situation for the World Health Organization, concluded that "In effect, the United States is covering up and sometimes subsidizing the opium traffic which it purports to be eradicating,"[33] —there has been, until quite recently, no testimony to this effect provided by American per-

14

sonnel directly involved in the traffic. But at the Winter Soldier Hearings in Boston on October 9, 1971, a former Green Beret sergeant told how he had worked for the C.I.A., buying opium from the Meo tribesmen in Laos and loading it onto Air America planes.[34] Air America, sometimes referred to as Air Opium, does most of its business with the C.I.A.

Some federal officials will concede that ten percent of the heroin on the American market comes from Southeast Asia; others admit to five percent. But whatever their estimates, none think that any appreciable amount is brought in by organized crime. "So far as we can tell," said a Bureau of Narcotics and Dangerous Drugs agent, "the stuff coming in from the Far East has been on a personal basis—you know, a guy is coming home and he figures to make some easy money with a pound or two."[35] And there has always been a small traffic carried on by merchant seamen between Hong Kong and the major West Coast ports. But there is now evidence that as early as 1965 American gangsters were in Southeast Asia arranging for heroin shipment to the U.S.[36] And some independent investigators believe that by the end of 1972 twenty-five percent of the heroin being sold in America will have originated in Southeast Asia.[37]

Whatever the exact figures are, it is not surprising that organized crime took a long time to become involved with the huge supplies available in Southeast Asia. Heroin traffic is a business and like any business strives to maximize profits and reduce risks. Thirteen thousand miles makes for a heavy transportation bill, a good deal heavier than the bill for the three thousand miles from Europe. Then too, there is far less commercial traffic from the Far East than from Europe, and with fewer people for the authorities to check out, there is more chance of dis-

15

covery. Moreover, businessmen involved in illicit trade are, as are the rest of us, more comfortable dealing with old familiar faces. The European and Near East traders are well-established, traditional firms. They have built solid, dependable reputations. As long as heroin is available from these sources, the American importers will be doing most of their business at the old stands. However, if our understandings with France and Turkey manage to put a serious dent in the supply, Southeast Asian heroin will naturally fill the gap, just as Arabian oil made up the deficit caused by overpriced American oil.

At this time the bulk of heroin feeding our addict population is still traveling a long-established route which originates in the poppy fields of Turkey.

In 1969 the Turkish Government estimated that 60,000 farmers were growing opium poppies, and it reported an opium crop of 117 tons to the International Narcotics Control Board.[38] It also reported a leakage of seven percent—or 8.19 tons—to the illicit market.[39] 8.19 tons is roughly 7,445 kilos, enough to manufacture approximately 750 kilos of heroin. In the same year, the Bureau of Narcotics and Dangerous Drugs maintained that 1,500 to 2,500 kilos of heroin were being smuggled into the country each year.[40] If the Bureau was correct, the Turkish Government underestimated their opium leakage by some 4,500 kilos. But neither the BNDD nor the Turkish government's estimates had much connection with reality. To begin with, the BNDD's 1,500 to 2,500-kilo figure was patently ludicrous. Even the upper figure would barely take care of the habits of the 68,000 heroin addicts the BNDD said existed, a number they themselves admitted was probably one hundred percent too low. As for the amount of heroin coming in: as of March 1971, agents of the BNDD's International Section estimated 20,000 kilos.[41] Since they and the rest of the BNDD claim that heroin traffic has increased at about ten percent a year over the past three or four years, the 1969 figure was probably closer to 16,000 or 17,000 kilos. And if the BNDD is correct in saying that eighty percent of the heroin here comes from Turkish opium, then more opium was being harvested in Turkey for the illicit market than for the licit one. 117 tons of opium converts into approximately 11,000 kilos of heroin, a figure considerably less than that needed to supply eighty percent of the American market.

Of course the Turkish farmers have good reason to sell as much as they can to the heroin dealers. Opium is their biggest—and in some cases, only—cash crop. The government monopoly pays them $12 per kilo; the traffickers pay from $25 to $35.[42] Few people can resist doubling their money, and a poor farmer can hardly afford not to. The Turkish Government, after agreeing to end opium production when the 1972 crop is in, seems to be having doubts, doubts about the money which they and the farmers will lose. A November 22, 1971 story in the New York *Times,* entitled "The Faltering War on Narcotics," contains the following:

> On January 6, 1970 . . . Washington reported progress in a program to pay Turkish farmers not to grow opium poppies . . . Now, nearly two years later, a Turkish Cabinet Minister says that the 35 million offered by the United States is absurdly inadequate; it would take ten times as much.

What the story didn't mention was *why* after being an adequate figure in January 1970, thirty-five million was then, in November 1971, "absurdly inadequate." The reason was quite simple: there were far more opium farmers in Turkey than the 60,000 the government knew about in 1969. Under a voluntary plan for the registration of opium farmers in 1970, 80,000 registered. Then, from June 1971 to November 1971 under a compulsory plan, more than 100,000 applied for licenses, and the number is expected to reach 150,000 by the end of the year.[43] And many observers believe there may be another 50 to 150,000 who *won't* register. The Turkish Government has not disclosed how, if the agreement is ever implemented, the money from America will be distributed, but it is hard to see how the money will or can be sufficient to offset the loss of income from the illicit market. For even in the unlikely event of the government's paying one hundred percent compensation to every opium farmer, the compensation will be at the government prices, not the illicit market prices. Human nature being what it is, a great many farmers will probably take the government's money *and* the trafficker's money.

And while Turkey is considering an official shutdown of poppy cultivation, Iran resumed poppy growing in 1969, after prohibiting it for thirteen years with little effect. The acreage cultivated in 1970 was doubled in 1971.[44]

Growing opium poppies is but the first stage on the heroin ladder. The various stages in manufacturing, shipping, and pricing from Turkey to New York are described below. There are other major ports of entry—Miami, Montreal, New Orleans—but New York is by far the largest. (This may be changing; according to recent reports, Miami is now rivaling New York.) It seems that half the heroin used in America is used in New York.

It must be stressed that almost no detailed information relating to the heroin traffic on any level above street-dealing is beyond dispute. Heroin is not the kind of business in which government agents get to examine the books. The general outline is probably correct, but specific quantities and prices are estimates and no more. They might be true for some shipments and some dealers, but not for others. [45]

- Crude opium is supplied by Turkish farmers to opium brokers at $25 per kilo. Some of the farmers are diverting part of their legal crop; others are growing solely for the illicit market.
- The brokers sell the crude opium to labs in Istanbul, Beirut, and Aleppo at a fifteen percent markup. The labs convert the crude opium into morphine base. Ten kilos of crude opium make one kilo of morphine base.
- The morphine base is sold to heroin refining labs at $500 per kilo. Until 1970 almost all of these labs, with the exception of a few in Beirut, Aleppo, and Rome, were located in the Marseilles area. Since 1970 the French authorities have applied increasing pressure in Marseilles, the chief result of which has been the establishing of heroin labs in Brussels, Amsterdam, Madrid, Zurich and outside Paris.
- The labs sell their finished product of eighty-five to ninety-five percent heroin for $2,000 per kilo to the brokers who arrange the bulk sales in the United States. The lab and the brokerage may be independent, but usually they are controlled by one management. The $2,000 figure applies only to those trading in bulk, say one hundred kilos or more. Most narcotic agents believe that fifty to sixty percent of the trade is conducted on this level, and the operators are French, Corsican, South American, and American gangs. The rest is done by independent dealers, from one to ten kilos at a time. There are a great number

of these independents. For a ten-kilo load, they probably pay $3,000 per kilo in Marseilles; for one key, $4,500. But it depends. Prices fluctuate relative to the particular situation.

- The major market is America, so the heroin must be smuggled in from Marseilles, Brussels, Paris or wherever the finished product has been processed and stored. On the independent dealer level, the smuggler is usually the dealer himself. On the bulk level, the operation is more in keeping with standard business procedure: the factory sells to the wholesaler and arranges for transportation to his warehouse. Under this arrangement, the landed price of a kilo of heroin is $6,000 to $10,000. The factory management is French and Corsican, the wholesalers South American and American. Where the Mafia fits in is not clear. According to Gay Talese, they got out of the heroin business in the early 1960s when the older Mafia men, who believed that it led to unnecessary exposure, asserted their authority over the younger men and stopped their heavy involvement in heroin. Others say that the Mafia only got out of wholesaling and the lower-level areas—and that they still remain as the bankers of the trade. (And heroin *needs* bankers as all big business needs bankers. A wholesaler in a hundred-kilo deal must put up—at $6,000 per kilo— $300,000 on signing the contract and the balance on delivery. In cash.) Still others, including some senior customs officials, believe the Mafia still operates on the wholesale level as well. They cite a '68 case in which a captured smuggler gave information indicating that the portion earmarked for the Mafia was priced forty percent lower than that going to other wholesalers. And to whom, ask these customs officials, do you give such special prices, except your biggest and best customer? (or your one and only bank?)

- Once in New York, the heroin is held by bulk buyers and independents until they can arrange the transfer to *their* regular customers, smaller wholesalers and jobbers. The hundred-kilo man will not usually sell in less than ten-kilo loads. The man buying at this level will pay from $10,000 to $13,000 per kilo. He in turn resells at $18,000 to $25,000 per uncut kilo.

- From this point to the street-dealing level, the picture becomes more complex. The ten-kilo man may have his own factory for cutting and packaging for the street, or he may not. If not, he might sell uncut keys as described or he might cut his load once to forty to forty-five percent heroin and sell a once-cut key for $18,000. And the one-kilo buyer might either run a factory or simply cut his key a time or two and sell half or quarter keys or even ounces. All of course suitably marked up. Apparently, this cutting a key once, or in most cases twice—so you have, for example, three thirty percent keys in place of one ninety percent key—is the standard practice when selling in one-kilo lots. A man able to buy only one kilo, can almost never buy a pure kilo.

There seems to me to be two obvious facts about the international traffic in heroin: (1) It is much larger and more diverse than anyone in official life is willing to admit; and (2) considering the extent and impact of it, very little hard information is known.

Depending on whom one talks to, what statistics one reads and what day one gets the information there are:

   I   A   13,000 pounds of heroin coming into the country each year.

21

B 25,000 pounds of heroin coming into the country each year.

C 44,000 pounds of heroin coming into the country each year.

II A Eighty percent comes from Turkish opium, five percent from Southeast Asia, fifteen percent from South America.

B Eighty percent Turkish, ten percent Southeast Asian, ten percent South American.

C Sixty-five percent Turkish, twenty-five percent Southeast Asian, ten percent South American.

D The major supplier is the People's Republic of China.

III A The Mafia controls the lion's share of the market, not directly, but through its banking operations.

B The Mafia has had little to do with heroin since the early sixties.

C The Mafia is in it on every level.

D The great bulk of the traffic is controlled by organized French, Corsican, Latin American, and American gangs.

E No more than fifty to sixty percent is controlled by organized crime; the rest by hundreds of small independents.

IV A "...huge seizures of heroin, in addition to causing appreciable financial losses to the traffickers...have had some effect on supply." Eugene T. Rossides, Assistant Secretary of the Treasury; October 1971.[46]

B "The impact [of seizures] has not been significant." Whitney North Seymour, U.S. Attorney for the Southern District of New York; November 1971.[47]

C "Impact, shit! There hasn't been a real panic since 1967, and the prices don't fluctuate either. You could take a hundred keys off the street tomorrow morning and everyone would have their shit tomorrow afternoon." New York Police Department undercover agent, November 1971.[48]

And though the paucity of documented information makes any conclusions on these questions at best educated guesses, the weight of what evidence there is, makes it likely that:

I   At *least* 44,000 pounds (20,000 kilos) of heroin enter the country each year. (And if the addict-user population estimates made in Chapter II are reasonably accurate, a good deal more than this may be coming in.)

II   Sixty-five percent is Turkish, twenty-five percent Southeast Asian, ten percent South American.

III No more than fifty to sixty percent is controlled by organized crime, the rest by small independents.

IV The seizures have made no noticeable impact on either supply or prices.

Further, I would say that only the last category appears likely to remain constant: for as long as there is a market where great profits can be made, someone will supply it. And there is no shortage of the basic material, opium.

As the market grows, and it *is* growing, more heroin will come in.

If and when more pressure is put on the Turkish supply, the primary source will gradually shift to Southeast Asia.

The nationality and type of trafficker will change

according to conditions. Eliminating one group—if this were possible—would only mean that another one would step in. Money breeds willing gamblers.

Before we discuss the street level—getting the product to the consumer—it might be worthwhile to see how much money is generated by the heroin trade *before* the retail markup. Here is a one-kilo progression from Turkey to New York, indicating the major points of markup:[49]

Turkey: 10 kilos crude opium at $25 . . . . $250
Lebanon: 1 kilo morphine base 500
France: 1 kilo heroin 2,000
New York: 1 kilo heroin at a median price of . . 15,500
                                                                              $18,250

Assuming 20,000 kilos are brought in each year—and I think this too low, for reasons which will be stated in the next chapter—heroin is at least a $365,000,000 business before it ever reaches the consumer. And it is at the consumer level where the truly outrageous markups occur. After all, before then, one deals with fellow businessmen, and there is sufficient competition to keep prices in line. On the street there is a captive market, an addict who *must* buy the product.

The addict in the street is what the heroin business is all about. Without him, the huge shipments entering the country wouldn't be worth a garageful of Edsels. But he is there and in numbers considerably in excess of the 100 to 200,000 the BNDD published in their official statements as late as the spring of 1972. (They now say there are 560,000.)[50] What follows is a transcript of one portion of a long conversation with three N.Y.P.D. Narcotics Bureau undercover men describing the retail setup.[51] They are not cops who disguise themselves as street people, but street people who became cops. I believe their information is accurate. It checks at every point with the information gathered from junkies and dealers.

Officer A: The lowest level is the accommodation man. He's a guy with a habit. What he does, he hangs around, he knows all the dealers in the neighborhood. You go up to him and ask, "Who's doin' anything?" and for a certain price, a couple of dollars, a couple of bags, he'll go buy the narcotics for you, bring it back to you, and then he'll have enough for his habit. He's not a regular day-to-day dealer, he's just a man who does you this favor. Maybe he does this for ten, twelve, fourteen people, you see. He's popular among the people from New Jersey. They come down to the city to cop drugs and they don't know anybody in the area, so they get an accommodation man, a junkie, and he'll take care of them.

So what's the next level?

Officer C: The next level is just the regular guy who's on junk. Maybe you've known me a long time, so you give me a bundle to off. As a result of me offing this bundle, you maybe give me three, four, five bags. Depends. Enough to take care of my habit, plus I off the stuff for you because you don't want to take the chance of offing it yourself.

Officer B: You go up a step and the guy may or may not have a habit. But he's not a big dealer. Maybe he deals a couple of half-loads.

What's a half-load?

Officer B: Usually fifteen bags—two-dollar, three-dollar, five-dollar. Whatever, it's still a half-load. He might deal a few of them, just to make a nice bundle. Or take care of his habit and some money besides. He either works

25

on the street or out of an apartment. He's small-time, unless he's got people dealing for him.

And that guy, the guy with people dealing for him?

Officer A: He's a lieutenant. This is a man, he'll have four, five, even up to a dozen men. These guys just described, they'll be out on the street dealing for him. And he'll go out maybe once or twice a day, pick up the money and give them their quotas for the day. Maybe three, four half-loads to sell. Usually two-dollar bags.

Usually you read about nickel ($5) bags.

Officer A: Depends on the area. In the schoolyards, a two-dollar bag is like two-fifths of a nickel bag, maybe one-half. Now in Harlem, though, it's different. A two-, three-dollar bag there is like a nickel bag in Times Square. Seven to ten percent heroin.

I've heard everywhere from three percent out in the suburbs to twelve to fourteen percent in Harlem and Bedford-Stuyvesant.

Officer C: The reason is, Harlem is more ready to have heroin. Therefore, a bigger market there—steady.

Officer A: And the competition is fierce. So quality goes.

And after the lieutenant?

Officer C: Well, then you got this guy who very seldom touches anything. He don't use. What he does: I make a big score from you, you give me my stuff, I pay you, I give it to my lieutenant and let him distribute it among his lower people.

What kind of quantities is he dealing in?

Officer C: Well, he's up to a kilo. Might buy a key, half a key, a quarter.

What's he usually pay if he just buys a key?

Officer C: About eighteen grand.

Officer A: Depends on the cut. The guy who's buying just a key is not getting pure heroin. He's buying it probably

26

twenty-five to thirty percent pure.

And about $18,000 for that?

Officer C: No, no. Maybe twelve or fourteen. Depends on what kind of customer he is. Better customer, better price. Sometimes even ten thousand.

Now, after this guy. Someplace the eighty-five to ninety percent stuff must be held.

Officer A: Now you go up into the business kind of operation. This man sits down in a restaurant, a bar, and talks business with two, three guys. They get their shipments once every three, four months. When it comes in, he has one guy pick up two keys, another four, and so on. He's got these steady customers. He only deals with them.

Where's the initial cutting, from the eighty-five to ninety percent stuff?

Officer A: The real big guys, they sell it as it comes in. The first cutting takes place at the level above the one-key guy. Like the guy we just been talking about, the ten-key guy. He gets ten pure keys and he does the initial cutting. He's got cutters, a factory operation. He'll have professional cutters, never junkie cutters. You only get junkie cutters further down the line. And if he doesn't have equipment to test the purity, he'll have junkies there to test it. An old-line junkie, who's shooting up just to keep from being sick. This kind of guy can get off one time and tell you how good the stuff is. He'll shoot and tell you, "Hit it one more time." Or he'll say, "Don't hit it no more, you'll spoil it."

There must be a lot of levels of cutting, then.

Officer A: Oh, yeah. After the first cut, the key guy will cut, the half-key, the quarter-key. Even the piece guys, the ouncers, they cut.

Officer B: You get some kid from Jersey, and maybe he'll buy a couple of nickel bags. And he'll go home and whack it up himself and sell it in New Jersey.

How's the quality control?

Officer A: Not good the way it used to be. Like somebody gets a piece, an ounce, and they tell him it's been scrambled already, but it wasn't. Somewhere along the line, somebody made a mistake and it wasn't cut. And it's like forty to fifty percent heroin. So the guy puts it out on the street, and what happens is, some kid who hasn't much of a habit—he's been shooting three percent stuff out in Mineola—and he gets this forty to fifty percent stuff and he's gone. That's it.*

Officer B: Most of the people who were dealing years ago, well, it was all organized. The mob, the organization, the Mafia, whatever you want to call it, they controlled things. And everything was strained through a porcelain sifter and was cut exact for the street level. They made it that way. Now you get people take a mayonnaise jar, put in the lactose, quinine, and the heroin, mix it up through a nylon stocking. Only the heroin might be all caked in one corner, you never know. But the guy just whacks it up anyway and puts it out on the street. No wonder we're getting so many o.d.'s.

How much cash does all this action generate from a

---

*There were 1,259 "narcotic-related" deaths in New York City in 1971.[52] It is not clear from the data released by the Chief Medical Examiner's Office precisely how many of these deaths were attributable to heroin overdoses, but it is clear that o.d.'s are not always a matter of shooting up a stronger dose than usual:

"Sudden collapse and death following intravenous injection has been reported in a number of . . . individuals. Such fatalities have often been attributed to overdose resulting from erratic and unexpected variations in the purity of drugs obtained from the black market. However, there is considerable evidence that many of these deaths are not merely due to overdose, but are a consequence of partly soluble contaminant substances in the sample and, perhaps, some drug hypersensitivity phenomenon."[53]

kilo of heroin? The reader can be excused if he guesses a sum anywhere from $225,000 to $1,000,000, which is the range I have encountered in just an hour's reading on the subject. The last figure is especially popular when police are citing the value of heroin confiscated in a raid. Anyway, here is a sampling of street values given for one kilo of heroin:

$272,000	The New York *Times,* Feb. 13, 1970
$225-500,000	*Forbes* Magazine, April 1970
$410,000	R.L. Lingeman, *Drugs from A to Z: A Dictionary,* 1969
$1,000,000	*Drugs,* Scott, Foresman and Company, 1969

As diverse as these figures are, they are not simply the products of fevered imaginations; they are the products of inadequate reporting and faulty arithmetic. To quote the Scott, Foresman and Company pamphlet,

> When this kilo is "cut," . . . the mixture ends up containing three or four percent heroin. A little arithmetic shows that, with such "cutting," the original kilo will grow into a product worth a million dollars on the illicit market.

A little arithmetic shows a quite different figure. But let's backtrack a bit. According to New York Police Department's Narcotics Lab, the typical street bag in Manhattan contains seven percent heroin in a five-grain mix. Put another way, there is one-third grain of pure heroin. Now, a kilo contains 15,400 grains. "Pure" heroin, however, is not pure. A kilo of "pure" heroin is usually eighty-five to ninety percent heroin. In an eighty-five percent kilo, therefore, there would be 13,090 grains of heroin or 13,090 x 3 seven percent bags of heroin. Let us round it out and say 40,000 seven percent bags. And let us apply a little arithmetic, as urged by the writers of *Drugs,* a pamphlet distributed for use in New York City's public school drug education programs. If with seven percent heroin you produce 40,000 bags, then with three percent heroin—the figure that would yield the greatest dollar return in the Scott, Foresman and Company calculation—you would produce 90,000 bags. At $5 per bag, the highest price in New York and not one you would likely receive for a three percent bag, a kilo would bring in $450,000. If the kilo were ninety-five percent heroin—the highest recorded percentage—you would realize ten percent more, or $495,000. A tidy sum to be sure, but hardly so tidy as the $1,000,000 confidently calculated in *Drugs*.

But as in most businesses, what is charged for the product depends on the market and the competition. When the consumer is knowledgeable and the competition strong, quality remains high and prices within reason. In Harlem, still the oldest and strongest heroin market in the country, the seven percent bag that will fetch $5 in Times Square, will go for $2, maybe $3. In short, a 40,000-bag kilo will realize at best $120,000 and more likely $80,000. At the other end of the scale, say, Babylon, Long Island, where any considerable use of heroin among the subur·banites is recent, and where a three percent bag will sell for $5, the same kilo will realize $450,000. One might think all available heroin would flow to Babylon and like communities across the country. After all, why be content with $80,000 when you can get $450,000? Again though, the answer is in standard business analysis: for every kilo you can sell in Babylon, you can sell a hundred in Harlem. Moving goods in volume is the way to get the biggest profits; for example, using an arbitrary $20,000 for the cost of the kilo, the Babylon dealer comes away with a gross profit of $430,000, whereas the volume Harlem dealer does $6,000,000 with his hundred keys.

Heroin, at whatever the estimated yield of a kilo at street level, generates an enormous amount of untaxed cash. If the 20,000 kilos that agents of the Bureau of Narcotics and Dangerous Drugs say is coming in each year, were sold at the lowest prices—$2 per seven percent bag—the yield would be $1,600,000,000. Add to this the $365,000,000 generated between Turkey and the United States, and you have a close to two-billion-dollar annual business. Of course only a portion of these 20,000 keys —probably no more than one-half of the estimated 10,000 keys sold in New York—is retailed at the lowest prices. The bulk of the remaining 15,000 keys is sold for twice the Harlem prices. Which means that the annual heroin trade in America is more than three and a half billion dollars. Probably a lot more, for there are good reasons to believe that the heroin trade is considerably larger than 20,000 keys.

A closing note for this chapter: Narcotics agents working in the streets of New York don't call the man selling heroin to the addict a "pusher." They call him a "dealer." It is a matter of correct labeling. People don't often *push* heroin. They don't have to. The heroin dealer has no need to search for customers; customers search for him. He has what they need.

And how does the customer ingest what he needs? There are four methods: smoking, snorting, skin-popping, and mainlining.

Smoking can be done in as many different ways as one can smoke tobacco, but the most popular smoking technique among American G.I.s in Vietnam is to extract some tobacco from the tip of a regular cigarette, replace it with heroin and light up. Smoking is commonplace in Vietnam, but seldom if ever practiced in the United States. To begin with, smoking is a very inefficient way of utilizing heroin, and to get a "good" high, smoking requires far more potent heroin than is available here. In Vietnam forty to fifty percent pure heroin is the common product; in America a user is lucky to get ten percent heroin. And second, heroin is far too expensive here to permit such a practice, even if good smoking heroin were available.

Snorting, inhaling heroin through the nostrils as one does snuff or cocaine, is more efficient than smoking, and is practiced on a limited scale. Many users get their first taste of heroin by snorting it. The taste is bitter and, for most users, nauseating. For this reason, plus its inefficiency and consequent greater cost for a high equivalent to that gotten from skin-popping or mainlining, snorting is not too popular.

Skin-popping, injecting the drug subcutaneously or intramuscularly, is the most common introduction to heroin. Unlike smoking or snorting, this technique requires paraphernalia and preparation of the heroin. The paraphernalia or works needed are a cooker—usually a spoon—a match and a syringe. The user heats up a mixture of heroin and water in the spoon in order to dissolve the heroin and make it suitable for injection. It is then drawn up into the syringe—sometimes through a cotton filter to remove gross impurities, sometimes not, depending on the urgency of the user's need and his carefulness or lack of it. The last step is shooting up, injection.

Mainlining, injecting heroin directly into the vein, requires the same works and preparation as skin-popping. In addition a belt or other suitable object is usually wrapped around the arm to distend a vein and facilitate injection. Since neither smoking, snorting, nor skin-popping utilizes heroin as efficiently as mainlining, the great cost of heroin in America has made mainlining the most common method of use here. All methods provide a high, a feeling of well-being and euphoria, for the four to six hours the drug is effective, but only mainlining gives the user an intense "rush" immediately following injection. The "rush" is often described in sexual terms: "it's like coming all over," or "it's like an orgasm in the stomach," and so on.

The Wonderful World
of the BNDD

> "The question is," said Alice, "whether you *can* make words mean so many different things."
>
> "The question is," said Humpty Dumpty, "which is to be master—that's all."

Had Alice been an American girl, her indignation might have been caused by the cavalier use of numbers rather than words. With the possible exception of the U.S.S.R., no nation appears so committed to the numbers game as ours. We are inundated with statistics covering every sector of our lives and fantasies. From the transparent fraud of "nine out of ten physicians consulted found cheese superior to bologna" to the latest consumer-price index, numbers are the spurious and ever-present stampmark of objectivity. As most commonly played by political and advertising pitchmen, the numbers game seldom demonstrates anything but the cynicism of the players. The President will sincerely assure us that the latest statistics indicate a "slowing of the wage-price spiral." Using the same statistics, George Meany will argue to the contrary. Confusing, to be sure, but most of us understand the game. What is more difficult to assay, however, is the use of quite different figures purporting to describe the same phenomena. The unemployment figures used by the government are not those used by labor unions. Each side selects the figures which best support its interests. We may know this; what we *don't* know, without specialized information, is which set of figures is closest to the truth.

This is the problem in the addict-user numbers game. Writing to dramatize industry's concern with the losses it suffers from heroin addiction, Samuel Feinberg says, "New York City's total [of addicts] could be as high as 300,000 to 400,000."[1] Writing from a rather different stance, Patrick Murphy, New York City Police Commissioner, says, "On the streets, in the hallways and on the roofs of this city are maybe 50,000—perhaps as many as 100,000—hard-drug addicts."[2] Only a handful of investigators have the knowledge required to evaluate these and the many other equally divergent pronouncements on the extent of the heroin-using population. And even they are in no position to give anything like precise figures. As John Holahan has written: "It is doubtful that the actual number of heroin addicts in the United States can ever be determined with present techniques of estimation."[3]

The difficulty, however, is not with the techniques, but rather with the conditions under which estimates must be made, conditions which make results gathered by even the best techniques open to serious question. Simply put, criminals are not in the habit of lining up to be counted. So long as the use of heroin is a criminal offense, we can never have an accurate count of heroin users. This state of affairs was recognized forty-four years ago by Terry and Pellens in their classic work, *The Opium Problem*: " . . . it would seem quite evident that there is no accurate knowledge as to the exact number of chronic opium users in the country today . . . ," they wrote; the chief reason being that "With the advent of prohibitory legislation and the consequent fear of legal involvement . . . even greater efforts were made by individuals to conceal their condition."[4]

Even before passage of the Harrison Narcotics Act of 1914, when there was no question of illegality impeding the collection of data, estimates of the addict population varied remarkably. Several head counts were made of opiate addicts—notably in Tennessee, Iowa, Michigan and Illinois—and estimates of the total number of addicts in the country, extrapolated from these surveys, ranged from 269,000 to more than 1,000,000.[5] Ten to fifteen years after the enactment of the Harrison Act, the estimates covered an even wider range. Kolb and Du Mez, the most prominent Public Health Service researchers, estimated about 110,000;[6] Terry and Pellens, taking note of all the data available, estimated 500,000[7]; and "the most popular guess by experts not associated with enforcement agencies, which appeared in the mass media, was between one-half and one million addicts; and the usual guess by the leader of America's most powerful antinarcotics organization, the International Narcotic Education Association, was over one million addicts, possibly as high as four million."[8]

Kolb and Du Mez calculated that addiction reached a peak in 1900 and then steadily declined. But whatever the validity of their conclusions for the period prior to 1914, they are of no value for the period after 1914, since they are based on the invalid assumption that the pattern of addiction was not influenced by illicit drugs:

> It is realized that some of the addicts who were deprived of narcotics as a result of the decrease in the quantities of the drugs imported legally turned to the use of smuggled material after 1915, but in our opinion the number that obtained their supplies from this source was at no time large enough to affect the direction of the trend of addiction.[9]

Given such an assumption, it is hardly surprising that Kolb and Du Mez were able to find addiction declining, particularly after 1914. Since no heroin is now imported legally and addicts are unable to obtain their drugs from illegal diversions from licit sources, the same assumption today

> . . . would lead one to conclude that addiction has virtually disappeared. What these authors failed to recognize in 1924 was that smuggled supplies had already become virtually the sole source of the addict's supply and that quantities of legally imported drugs had become totally irrelevant.[10]

The Kolb-Du Mez study is of particular interest because its findings were apparently used by the Bureau of Narcotics (until April 8, 1968, the Bureau of Narcotics and Dangerous Drugs was called the Bureau of Narcotics) to develop what Alfred Lindesmith calls the ski-jump curve. This is a graph allegedly representing the history of narcotic addiction in the United States. Starting from a high point in 1914 of 200,000 (one in 400 of the total population addicted)—a figure which according to Lindesmith is admittedly based on " . . . a very limited survey made in Michigan and reported in 1878 by O. Marshall"[11] —it hits bottom at 20,000 in 1945, takes off to 60,000 (one in 3,000 of the total population addicted) in the early fifties and once again begins a gradual decline.

In addition to the fact that the Bureau's graph representing the history of addiction in the United States uses as a starting point a limited study from one state that could hardly be extended nationwide even at the time of the study, let alone thirty-six years later, it suffers from the further improbability, as Lindesmith has pointed out, of suggesting,

> . . . without making any allowance for the appearance of new addicts, that about 42,000 addicts vanished between 1914 and 1925, about 96,000 between 1925 and 1935, and approximately 42,000 between 1935 and 1945. When new and younger addicts are not being recruited in sufficient numbers to replace older addicts who die or quit the habit, it necessarily follows that the average age of the addicted population must increase. However, it is well known that between 1915 and 1945 the average age of known addicts declined considerably, and this demonstrates that we must assume a constant stream of new addicts being addicted each year. . . . Additional difficulties arise with the curve if one tries to take into account the fact that in 1915 women addicts outnumbered men about three to two and whites outnumbered Negroes around nine to one, whereas in 1945

39

male addicts outnumbered females about five or six to one and whites outnumbered Negroes only about three to one. From considerations of this sort alone, it is evident that the Bureau's ski-jump curve is mainly a fantasy and has little relation to reality.[12]

The Bureau's public performance in estimating the addict population since the days of the ski-jump curve has not borne much more relation to reality. From 1955 to 1968 the figures 48,000 and 60,000 were used almost interchangeably by Bureau officials testifying before Congressional committees or making statements to the press. In its own publications the Bureau apparently prefers more precise figures. "At the close of 1969," states *Fact Sheets,* a product of the Bureau, "some 68,088 active narcotic addicts were recorded,"[13] an increase of 4,077 since Dec. 31, 1968, when the BNDD reported 64,011 addicts in the United States.[14] A comparison of these figures, insofar as it reflects an increase in the addict population, must be considered a concession to reality, however limited. But the long years of indulging in fantasy have made other government agencies skeptical of Bureau statistics. For example, after dutifully stating the Bureau's December 31, 1968 figure, one government publication makes the disclaimer "these figures only include those addicts reported to the Bureau" and then goes on to say

> The heroin abuse problem has been increasing since World War II and it continues to increase. Perhaps the most realistic estimate of the number of opiate addicts in the country is between 100,000 and 200,000.[15]

The reluctance of the BNDD to make realistic estimates of the addict population is understandable, for any realistic estimate clearly indicates a basic flaw in the Bureau's method of fighting opiate addiction. Efficacious methods would lead to a decline in addiction, not to an increase. The hypocritical use of incorrect figures, though a great aid in covering up a misconceived policy of repression, leads to certain difficulties. The Bureau's "success," as demonstrated by its ski-jump curve and subsequent understatements of the addict population, would, in any rational context, have lead to a call for a reduction of the Bureau's budget. To forestall so terrible a possibility, Anslinger and his successors, Giordano and Ingersoll, resorted to hyperbole when describing every other aspect of the drug problem. Addicts were painted as monsters, the country in imminent danger of drowning under a flood of Red Chinese heroin, and, just in case the Congress might fail to get properly exercised over 60,000 addicts, the horrors of marijuana were always vividly depicted.

In recent years, with o.d. rates jumping all over the country, with newspapers in major cities carrying heroin stories on an almost daily basis and with citizens and politicians demanding something be done about the heroin problem, the BNDD has used more realistic figures. But it is still reluctant to face up to the true size of the problem. Dr. Joseph Greenwood, a BNDD statistician, has estimated 315,000 addicts in the country. This estimate was based on 1968 data, and Dr. Greenwood had his estimate prepared by 1969, but it didn't reach the public until late 1971 and then only on an "unofficial" basis. (Meanwhile, the Bureau was putting out estimates of 68,088, and other government agencies were citing 100,000 to 200,000.)

Dr. Greenwood's statistical model multiplies the number of known users who could be rearrested by the ratio of total heroin arrests to the numbers of known users included in those arrests. Translated, this means that on the assumption "that the true number of addicts for a given year can be estimated from the number of addicts reported

that year and in previous years"[16] the equation that yields
this result is

$$A = R \times \frac{a}{r} \text{ where}$$

A = the actual number of addicts in a given year
(period 2)

R = the number of addicts registered with the BNDD in
the previous year (period 1)

a = the total number of addicts registered with the
BNDD in period 2

r = the number of addicts registered with the BNDD in
period 1 who are arrested in period 2.

Or, to use actual figures:

$$A\,(315,000) = R\,(63,000 \times \frac{a\,(60,000)}{r\,(12,000)}$$

The major shortcomings of this method are obvious.
Using a factual assumption cited by Dr. Greenwood himself, "... that not all addicts are either known to law
enforcement agencies, or even if known, not all such
people have been reported to the BNDD,"[17] one need
only suppose that instead of R=63,000, R=100,000, and
the equation yields 500,000 addicts instead of 315,000.
Dr. Greenwood takes care of this possibility with yet
another assumption, which is simply that the probability
of any given addict being arrested in any given year is
precisely the same regardless of whether he had been
arrested in the previous year or not.[18] Thus, if R were in
fact 100,000, the equation would still yield 315,000 rather
than 500,000, since with the probability of arrest remaining constant, the value of r would rise concomitantly.

The trouble here is that not only is there no evidence
given to justify this assumption, but that all evidence
points in the opposite direction. Once an addict has been
arrested, he is known to the police and his chances of

being under surveillance in the future are much increased. And of course his chances of being rearrested. Moreover, anyone familiar with the tactics of narcotics officers knows perfectly well that when arrests are needed, it is the addicts known to them who are picked up.

A few months after Dr. Greenwood's estimate belatedly surfaced, the BNDD suddenly discovered an additional 245,000 addicts roaming the countryside. In a published interview Myles J. Ambrose, head of the Justice Department's new Office for Drug Abuse Law Enforcement, cited a remarkable revision of the BNDD's estimate of the addict population. Here is Mr. Ambrose speaking in the April 3, 1972 edition of *U.S. News and World Report*:

> As of 1960, the Bureau of Narcotics estimated that we had somewhere in the neighborhood of 55,000 heroin addicts ... I think the estimates were reasonably correct. ...
> Then we had the tremendous explosion of drug abuse of the 1960's commencing around 1962-63. ...
> The Bureau of Narcotics and Dangerous Drugs ... said that they estimate now the figure to be 560,000 addicts.[19]

In short, according to Mr. Ambrose and the BNDD, there has been a ten-fold increase over the past ten years. In truth it is merely a case of the BNDD's keeping abreast of the political necessities of the times, which in this instance demand some realism concerning the extent of the heroin problem. A Congress that appropriated seventeen million dollars for drug law enforcement in 1969 could hardly be persuaded to vote 229 million dollars for the same in 1973 unless the Bureau's figures matched the voters' outcry for action.

As for the ten-fold increase, this is just another BNDD statistical fantasy made possible by the wild underestimates of the past. There has been a steady increase over the years, but no present data indicates one of 1,000 percent. Indeed, a page later in the interview Mr. Ambrose apparently denies there has been *any* increase. Responding to the interviewer's statement that "the drug problem keeps increasing," Mr. Ambrose says,

> No, I really wouldn't put it that way. What I say is that we've had many years of neglect in trying to cope with this problem. We are now just getting the resources needed. [20]

This statement suggests that the real problem has been the grievous underfinancing of the BNDD and other federal drug agencies during two previous Democratic administrations—though to my knowledge Congress has never given the BNDD less than what it asked for—while avoiding any hint that perhaps what has been wrong all along is the whole punitive philosophy of the BNDD.

To return to Dr. Greenwood, his estimate of 315,000 does not take into account the data to be found in New York City's Narcotics Register, the most thorough listing of addict-users in the country. Indeed, when telephoned in the fall of 1971, he was surprised to learn that such a listing existed. (I suspect—without being able to verify the suspicion—that the BNDD's later 560,000 estimate is based on raw data from the Register. Ambrose mentions "new samples" and "new methods," and people at the Register recall recent inquiries from a Treasury Department Senior Economist.) Notwithstanding this previous official ignorance, the Narcotics Register data is by far the most complete in the country, and any serious attempt to estimate the heroin-using population must start with it.

The compilers of the Register are well aware that is it not a complete listing of the city's addict-users, and they are well aware of certain methodological shortcomings. Namely that:

1 the reports come from many sources—police, courts, hospitals, Department of Welfare, treatment programs, schools, private practitioners, etc.—and are not of equal quality.

2 there are agencies and private practitioners who do not report to the Register. One example of this, to quote the 1969 Statistical Report from the Register: " ... the public education authorities have only recently agreed to begin to report and it is believed that the number of young people in the current files is significantly underestimated."[21]

(The chief reason for this reluctance to report is very understandable. For though the provisions of Section II of the New York City Health Code do not allow the disclosure of individual names listed in the Register, even under subpoena, laws can always be changed—and some educators and doctors are reluctant to expose their students and patients to possible future jeopardy. The majority of school principals, however, seem reluctant to report for a more selfish reason: they feel disclosure of a high incidence of narcotic use in their schools would reflect adversely on them and damage their careers. The Narcotics Register is still, as of March 1972, getting very little data from New York schools.[22])

3 at the present time the cases in the Register are removed only in the event of death. Those under treatment, those in jail, those who have moved out of the city, and those who may have stopped using remain listed in the Register. (According to New York City's Addiction Services Agency, there are, as of March 1972, some 28,193 persons in various

treatment programs around the city—15,577 of them on methadone.[23] No one really knows, but probably no appreciable numbers have moved out of the city—heroin users simply don't like to leave the sources of their supplies. The number who voluntarily quit using is always very small.)

The Narcotics Register data is a shock to anyone whose knowledge of the addict-user population has been limited to BNDD reports. From 1964, when it began its work, through 1968 it accumulated 58,095 unduplicated names of narcotics users. These included some 12,000 new names in 1968. By the end of 1969 the total had reached 94,699—36,604 new names.[24] By the end of 1970 the Register had listed 150,000 unduplicated names, with approximately 55,000 new names. (The 1970 Statistical Report has not been published as of this writing. Minor data is still being added; thus the rounded-off figures.) Preliminary analysis of the 1971 data indicates another 50,000 new names will be listed.[25]

When the 1971 figures are completed, then, the Narcotics Register will carry approximately 205,000 unduplicated names of narcotics users, which, if one removes the numbers in treatment or in jail, would give roughly the 150,000 heroin users in New York City estimated by Dr. Greenwood. Unfortunately, this coincidental statistical symmetry doesn't exist in fact. All users are not reported to the Register, and studies have been made to determine just how many are unreported. The Assistant Medical Examiner for New York, Michael Baden, in 1968 and the Narcotics Register's Lawrence Bergner and Sherman Patrick in 1970 checked the death certificates of known addicts against the Register list to see how many of them were indeed listed. The rationale, as stated by Bergner and Patrick, was that "The establishment of a relationship between the cases (of death) known and not known to the Register should make it possible to develop a model for estimating the number of unreported cases and to refine prevalence estimates."[26] That is, since addicts clearly die whether they are in the Register or not, the number of them previously unreported to the Register should, if they are the same kind of addicts as in the Register, indicate the proportion of all unreported addicts. Being a logically sound methodology, it should.

Baden found that fifty percent of heroin users who die in New York are listed in the Register.[27] Bergner and Patrick found only thirty-seven percent listed in their 1970 study of 553 cases. Moreover, they reported that "when the age, sex, and ethnic characteristics of deaths were compared to the total Register population of heroin abusers, there was no significant difference."[28] A more recent study of death certificates done at the Register duplicated Baden's fifty percent finding and also turned up one significant difference between the unlisted death certificate population and the Register population: there was a higher incidence of young people, particularly those under fifteen, among the death certificate population. This finding supports what the Register already knew: that it gets very little reporting from the schools.[29]

It would appear that no more than fifty percent of the heroin users in New York City are listed in the Narcotics Register. If all *were* listed, the Register would carry as of December 31, 1972, 410,000 unduplicated names. Subtract from this a generous 50,000 for those in treatment, in jail, no longer in the city or no longer using heroin, and you are left with 360,000 heroin users in New York looking for their next fixes.

It is commonly asserted that one-half of the heroin users in America live in New York City. The basis for this assertion is that one-half of the users reported to the BNDD are residents of New York. Since the BNDD's published addict estimates prior to Ambrose's statement are fantasies, there is no way of knowing whether this assertion is true or not. But let us suppose it is true, and let us make another assumption, namely that a similar proportion of the heroin users in other locales are either under treatment or in jail. It follows that there are at least 720,000 untreated users at large in the country.

I personally believe this to be a conservative estimate. But this belief, though supported by many knowledgeable people, *is* a belief and nothing more. The addict-user population is growing each year, and it is growing younger each year, but its true size is unknown.

The size of the addict-user population provides a good indication of the amount of heroin smuggled into the country each year to supply its needs. John F. Holahan in *Dealing With Drug Abuse,* a report to the Ford Foundation—using data developed by the Hudson Institute on the consumption habits of American heroin users (in terms of number of bags per day per addict) and the amount of heroin in a typical street bag, and an estimate of the addict-user population apparently derived from the BNDD —estimates that 4,456 kilos of pure heroin are consumed each year by American addict-users.[30]

This quite ludicrous underestimate comes not from improper methodology, but from two highly inaccurate premises. Namely that the number of addict-users in the country is 250,000 and that 80,000 street bags containing an average of ten milligrams of pure heroin are usually obtained from a kilo.[31] Accepting the Hudson Institute data on consumption habits as reasonable estimates, but correcting Mr. Holahan's factual errors, one arrives at a much greater amount of heroin being used than does Mr. Holahan.

To begin with, let us replace the mythical one hundred percent pure heroin with real heroin, which ranges from eighty-five to ninety-five percent pure. Using a mean of ninety percent, we turn the 4,456 kilos of mythical heroin into 4,901 kilos of actual heroin. Second, the number of addict-users in the country seems to be at least 720,000, not 250,000. For simplicity's sake, let us say that Mr. Holahan underestimated by a factor of three. Multiplying 4,901 by three gives us 14,703 kilos of heroin. And third, according to narcotics officers and heroin dealers in New York City, the typical street bag contains approximately twenty-two milligrams of pure heroin (seven percent by weight), which translates to 40,000 bags per kilo—not Mr. Holahan's 80,000 bags. The underestimate factor here is two, so multiplying 14,703 by two gives us 29,406 kilos of heroin being consumed in America each year. It seems safe to assume that at least this much is smuggled in each year. As noted earlier, there have been no heroin panics for some time.

As noted above, we can never know the full extent of heroin use so long as heroin users are defined as criminals under the law, but using the Narcotics Register and the work of Terry and Pellens, we can get a pretty clear picture of how the pattern of narcotic use has changed since the enactment of the Harrison Narcotics Act of 1914 and the subsequent criminalization of the narcotics user.

Prior to Harrison:

I   Females greatly outnumbered males.[32]

> In an 1878 Michigan survey of 1,313 narcotics users, 803 or 62.2 percent were women.
> In an 1880 Illinois study of 235 opium users, 169 or 71.9 percent were women.

In an 1885 Iowa study of 235 narcotics users, 149 or 63.8 percent were women.

In an 1913 Florida study of 541 narcotics users, 313 or 58.9 percent were women.

In a 1914 Tennessee survey of 2,370 narcotics users, 1586 or 66.9 percent were women.

II The average age of narcotics users was over forty.[33]

C.H. Earle in an 1880 Chicago, Illinois study reported the average age of his sample to be 39.7.

J.M. Hull in an 1885 Iowa study reported an average age of 46.5.

L.P. Brown in a 1914 Tennessee survey reported an average age of fifty.

III Whites greatly outnumbered blacks.[34]

In Terry's 1913 study of 541 Jacksonville, Florida cases, 134 or 24.8 percent were black, and this in a total population where blacks slightly outnumbered whites.

In Brown's 1914 statewide survey of Tennessee, "not over ten percent of the cases were colored."

IV Among narcotics users the affluent were overrepresented and the poor underrepresented. That opiate addiction was a predominantly middle- and upper-class vice was so taken for granted that almost no studies of the issue were made.

B.H. Hartwell in 1889 sent questionnaires to druggists representing 180 cities and towns in Massachusetts, asking the question "What classes of people use opium in your community?" with the following results:

"446 answers: 22 percent, all classes; 22 percent, middle classes; 7 percent, upper classes; 7 percent, lower classes; . . . 20 percent, miscellaneous. Of the remaining twenty-two percent,

50

eleven percent did not know of any opium use in their communities.[35]

He also asked the same question of 260 physicians representing one hundred cities and towns in the state:

"166 answers: 30 percent, all classes; 22 percent, higher; 3 percent, middle; 6 percent, lower; 12 percent, middle and higher; 14 percent, nervous women; 8 percent, do not know."[36]

V Virtually no crime was associated with narcotics use. To begin with, narcotics use was perfectly legal. And with morphine selling for sixty cents a dram[37] and opium at comparable prices and both available at the corner drugstore, there clearly was no need to engage in criminal activity in order to acquire the means to supply a habit. A dram contains sixty grains, and an average habit of three grains a day would cost three cents. Even a large habit, say ten grains, would be an insignificant expense.

A nineteenth-century American doctor urged that alcoholics and problem drinkers switch to opium or morphine. For, as he said, not only would they do far less damage to their bodies and families (opiate addicts didn't have any problems holding their jobs in those days), but in addition their change of habit would greatly benefit the community, since they would no longer engage in the violence and other asocial acts attendant to heavy drinking but notably absent among opiate users.[38]

A perusal of the Narcotics Register reveals a startlingly different picture today:

I Males greatly outnumber females.[39]

Of the 94,699 narcotics users listed at the end of

1969, 78,683 or 83.1 percent were men.

II The average age is under twenty-five.[40]

    87,848 or 92.9 percent are under forty.

    52,463 or 53.5 percent are under twenty-five.

    20,709 or 21.9 percent are under twenty, a figure that would be considerably higher if the under-fifteens were adequately reported.

Also, narcotics use is beginning at progressively earlier ages. Analyzing the Register data for the ages when users were first reported yields the following:

Between 1964-68 17.5 percent of the new listees were 15-19

    In 1969   26.8 percent of the new listees were 15-19
Between 1964-68 31.5 percent of the new listees were 20-24

    In 1969   36.8 percent of the new listees were 20-24
Between 1964-68 20.4 percent of the new listees were 25-29

    In 1969   17.4 percent of the new listees were 25-29
Between 1964-68 13.3 percent of the new listees were 30-34

    In 1969   8.0 percent of the new listees were 30-34
Between 1964-68   8.1 percent of the new listees were 35-39

    In 1969   4.9 percent of the new listees were 35-39
Of the 36,604 new cases reported in 1969, then, 63.6 percent were under twenty-five, as contrasted to 49 percent of those listed between 1964-68. And this despite, to repeat, the serious underreporting of the under-fifteen group.

III Blacks and Puerto Ricans greatly outnumber whites.[41]

    Of the 94,699 persons on the Register at the end of 1969,

41,553 or 43.9 percent were black.

30,539 or 32.2 percent were white.

20,634 or 21.8 percent were Puerto Rican.

IV Most addict-users are from low income groups.[42]

The Register does not provide a breakdown on the social-economic classes of the listees as such, but it does analyze them according to boroughs and by health districts within these boroughs. Since readers not thoroughly familiar with New York cannot be expected to have an intimate knowledge of its poorest areas, I shall list only those frequently mentioned in or on the national media.

> Manhattan: 45.3 percent are from Central and East Harlem;
>
> 24.8 percent from Lower East and Lower West Sides;
>
> 15.4 percent from Riverside.
>
> Bronx: the three worst areas—Morrisania, Mott Haven, and Tremont—account for 76.7 percent of the listees.
>
> Brooklyn: Bedford Stuyvesant, Brownsville, Ft. Greene, Red Hook, Bushwick, and Williamsburg-Greenpoint account for 72.5 percent of the listees.
>
> Queens: Jamaica, Flushing, and Corona account for 73.8 percent of the listees.

V Virtually nothing *but* crime is associated with heroin use.

> Right off, using heroin is a crime.
>
> Given the street price of heroin, all but a very tiny minority of users must employ criminal means to acquire the money for their drugs. They must either steal, sell their bodies, or sell heroin.

To sum up: Before the criminalization of the narcotics

user, a rough profile of the American narcotics-using population reveals a two-to-one proportion of women, an average age of over forty, preponderantly white, largely the affluent or relatively affluent classes, and little if any crime associated with narcotics use.

After the users' situation changed legally, the profile changed radically: an approximately five-to-one proportion of men, an average age well under twenty-five, preponderantly non-white, preponderantly poor, and a great deal of crime associated with narcotics use.

It would require a volume of impressive dimensions to illustrate fully and properly analyze the reasons why, in a span of less than sixty years, the typical opiate-user changed from a middle-class white woman to a poor black male. I don't have this detailed knowledge, and I doubt if I will ever have the stamina to acquire it. Still, I can point to some of the more obvious reasons.

The single greatest factor was the passage of the Harrison Narcotics Act of 1914. What Harrison did, or rather what the misapplication of Harrison did—for it was never intended to make nonmedical use of narcotics illegal, but rather to *regulate* such use—was to change completely the recruitment pattern of nonmedical opiate users.

Prior to 1914 the great majority of addicts were enlisted through medical prescriptions and quasi-medical patent medicines. Opium and morphine were generously prescribed for a large number of ailments ranging from menstrual cramps to dysentery. Menstrual cramps being commonplace, many women became addicts. An incredible range of patent medicines based on opium were used as home remedies for an even wider range of minor troubles. Then too, since it was socially unacceptable for women to drink alcohol, one can easily imagine them finding relief from their anxieties in bottles of Dr. Brown's

Magic Elixir. And when opium and morphine were at last found to be addictive, a new range of patent medicines based on heroin were advertised and sold as cures for addiction. And sure enough, they did take people off opium and morphine.

In short, most of the addicts prior to 1914 became addicted through professionally prescribed or self-prescribed opiates whose initial use was therapeutic. The Harrison Act

> ... had the effect ... of drastically reducing the flow of new addicts from medical practice or through the use of legal drugs. On the other hand, by shutting off the supply of legal drugs from countless users without criminal records it forced them to the illicit traffic and into the underworld.[43]

When trafficking with the underworld became a necessity for many people, addiction among middle-class white women fell off. As a class they were in no way suited, either by experience or upbringing to handle such a situation or to take such risks. Thus the rate of recruitment of new addicts among this class dropped sharply, and as time passed they became a minority rather than a majority. Of course those already addicted at the time of Harrison didn't have much choice: they were either able to get the drugs they needed from family doctors or they bought in the illicit market. By 1930 doctors who prescribed opiates to addict patients were being so fiercely persecuted by the Bureau of Narcotics that all but an insignificant handful refused to aid their former patients.[44] The few who did were the brave and the greedy.

The result was that the illicit traffic which began by servicing the unlucky who couldn't get prescriptions and the poor who couldn't afford doctors, ended up selling to almost all the addicts in the country. The urban ghettos were the natural market place for this product. Opiates moved in as soon as Harrison made it necessary to get a doctor's prescription. Then, as the possibilities widened in response to the repression, there was a large labor pool available to work on the most exposed and dangerous level—selling to the user. The people who do such work are those with the greatest need for money, a need unlikely to be met in any other way. That these people happened to be the blacks in the city ghettoes was not accidental but the legacy of our history.

In the beginning there was not any undue addiction among the blacks themselves. As late as 1945 white heroin addicts still outnumbered blacks by three to one. But with the constant exposure to heroin that was too common in the ghettos, it was inevitable that the addiction rates soared. For one thing, people are curious: they try the products that are around. Second, someone who tried heroin and liked it because he found it relieved his anxieties, tensions, feelings of inadequacy, and any number of other emotional difficulties, provided an incentive for his friends and associates; they witnessed his new sense of well-being and tried heroin to see if it would do the same for them. And third, the life of the addict-user, with its buying, selling and strongly focused hustling, provided a far more demanding and exciting career than the typical addict-user had any hope of finding in the legitimate world.

I think it only fitting to end this chapter by underlining the single greatest irony of the changes made by the Harrison Act. Before Harrison, the typical, relatively affluent addict could supply her needs for three cents a day. After Harrison, in 1972, the typical poor, black addict must pay $30 daily for his needs. If this weren't so shamefully obscene, one could cry at human folly.

The
Addict Personality

As we have seen, the current addict-user population in America is very different from that which existed prior to the Harrison Narcotics Act. This radical change—from a typically white, middle-class female to a typically black, slum-dwelling male—has been an important factor in the production of a wide range of mythology concerning the heroin user. What usually happens is that a white professional—doctor, psychiatrist, social worker or whatever—looks at and interprets the behavior of people whose backgrounds and social values are quite different from his and proceeds to draw conclusions about them based on his own value system.

An equally important factor in myth production is that the activities necessary to support heroin use lead many observers to confuse the effects of operating under criminal sanctions with the causes leading to addiction. Thus we have numerous pronouncements indicating that heroin users are drawn from the antisocial criminal segment of society, whereas in fact the large majority of users engage in criminal activity only because society gives them no other alternatives to procure the drugs they need.

And though the difficulties most professionals have in understanding and correctly characterizing addict-users has been greatly exacerbated by the changes in the user population, color and economic differences between investigator and subject are not the only reason why this is so. The simple fact that the user is doing something the investigator doesn't do, and with which he can rarely empathize, in itself leads to distortion. Long before whites became a minority of the heroin-using class, investigators had trouble being objective: "Excluding the few normal persons who become addicted through medical treatment, drug addicts are recruited from the ranks of the mentally ill."[1] So wrote Lawrence Kolb, referring to a study he had made in

1924 of 230 opiate addicts. His breakdown of the 230 cases is instructive:

14 percent were "mentally healthy"
13 percent were "criminal psychopaths"
13.5 percent were "psychoneurotics"
21.5 percent were "inebriates"
and 38 percent were "hedonistic, unstable types"[2]

Assuming Kolb was correct in classifying 26.5 percent as psychopaths and "psychoneurotics," we can say without fear of contradiction that this 26.5 percent were mentally ill. But we can hardly be so confident respecting the remaining 59.5 percent who were not "mentally healthy." Kolb doesn't say the 21.5 percent "inebriates" were alcoholics as well as opiate addicts, and since true alcoholism and opiate addiction don't usually go together —though heavy drinking and addiction often do—we can safely assume they were simply drinkers, perhaps even heavy drinkers. And it is a very wide, almost meaningless, definition of mental illness that categorizes a drinker, solely on the basis of his drinking, as mentally ill. But the fascinating and truly revealing classification is that of the 38 percent who, according to Kolb, were mentally ill because they were "hedonistic, unstable types." That is, you are mentally ill if you seek pleasure in heroin and, as a consequence of the life-style imposed by the laws of the land, are unable to lead a nine-to-five existence. Put another way, if you are unlike me, you are sick.

So be it. Let us now look at a sampling of mythology and try to find where the truth lies. Hopefully, we may learn something about why one person becomes a user and another, with equal opportunity, does not. But on this point we cannot expect to learn very much at present. It is an area where little is known and where much needs to be done.

One of the oldest myths is that a prospective user is given free samples by a vicious dope peddler who is seeking to enlarge his market—he is "... commonly offered the drug free ..."[3] and "... a drug peddler or pusher may give away the first dose to initiate a habit and hence a customer."[4] That this fantasy still persists is a tribute to the indestructibility of mythology, however ill-grounded. Perhaps its long life is attributable to the popular appeal of Nelson Algren's *The Man with the Golden Arm,* wherein the hero Frankie finds that while his initial shots were very cheap, they are becoming progressively more expensive as his habit and need grow. Or maybe Harry Anslinger's frequent depictions of the unprincipled pusher "hooking" his victims is to blame. Or conceivably the very widespread use of the term "pusher," with its connotation of passing the drug from the habitue to the neophyte, has played a large role. In any case there never was and there is not now anything but a very scanty factual basis for the story. So far as I know, the only evidence to support it has come from the occasional junkie hoping to mitigate a jail sentence by describing himself as the victim of a pusher looking for customers. Junkies not under this constraint tell a different story.

Almost all began using heroin through friends who were already using it, and far from it being the case that their friends gave them free samples or were even eager to initiate them, most junkies relate stories of having to convince their friends to sell them a snort or shot at cost. Naturally, there are exceptions, users eager to turn on their friends in much the same way as the social drinker presses a glass into your hand and the grass smoker a joint. But with heroin this is relatively rare and apparently occurs, when it does occur, only among white upper-middle-class users who can afford to do so. In the more common heroin scene, turning people on with free samples is both too expensive and too dangerous to be seriously contemplated. A Harlem dealer giving away free samples would be deluged by an eager horde, most of whom would be confirmed users swearing they had never so much as seen the stuff before. Then of course this prince of dealers would quickly become an extraordinarily famous personage in the community, and such public notoriety is not what a heroin dealer seeks. And even if all takers were neophytes, giving away samples in order to create habits and hence enough customers to make the scheme economically feasible, is a fantasy only someone thoroughly unfamiliar with addiction could entertain. And addiction is something with which dealers are quite familiar.

It usually takes a couple of weeks of shooting two bags a day of good junk to acquire any noticeable physical dependence. Let's say ten days at ten dollars a day, or one hundred dollars. Such an investment in future trade might be reasonable on the part of the dealer if, as some still believe, "the addiction probability for heroin is almost 100 percent."[5] But the addiction probability for heroin is nothing like 100 percent. If it were, our already large heroin problem would be beyond belief. In an urban ghetto it is difficult not to know someone who either uses or sells heroin. Anyone there, if he is curious, can obtain an introduction to the drug. He has a friend who is a user or an addict, or he has a friend who has a friend, and so on.

> It seems likely that a large percentage of the young black males in any large urban lower-class area have tried heroin. The majority who have experimented with it have not become addicted.[6]

The popular notion that "the opiate narcotic experience is intrinsically so pleasurable, or that physiological dependence develops so rapidly, that most who are subjected to it are promptly addicted is without support."[7] Isador Chien and others report an experiment in which 150 male volunteers in good health were given injections of morphine. Three and only three were willing to allow further injections, and none of these said he would have sought further morphine on his own. Another investigator reported that only ten percent of a normal group liked the experience they had on morphine.[8]

The above two experiments were conducted with morphine, but because of the similarity between the pharmacological properties of heroin and morphine, they are applicable here. Indeed most heroin users can't distinguish between equipotent doses of these drugs if not taken intravenously. And at least one very careful, double-blind experiment was conducted with heroin.[9] The results:

Of nine cases given two milligrams of heroin,
1 was enthusiastic about the experience,
2 found heroin slightly pleasant but with practically no effect,
3 found heroin neither pleasant nor unpleasant,
3 found heroin mildly unpleasant.

It is worth noting that a two-milligram dose is one-fifth the size of that contained in, according to some official sources,[10] an average Harlem street bag. Other sources, including the New York City Police Department, say that two milligrams is no more than one-tenth the dose contained in an average Harlem street bag. The size of the dose gains added significance when you consider that,

Of the eleven cases given four milligrams of heroin,
2 found no detectable effect,
2 found the experience mildly pleasant,
7 found the experience distinctly unpleasant.

And it is likely there would be more and more strongly stated negative experiences, if the doses were as potent as Harlem street doses.

As the Task Force Report of the President's Commission on Law Enforcement and the Administration of Justice (1967) states: ". . . opiates are not inherently attractive, euphoric, or stimulant substances."

Not attractive to most people, that is, if they are not in pain. But as anyone who has lain suffering in a hospital bed knows, a shot of morphine can be very attractive indeed. And it is this analgesic power of the opiates that has led many to believe that the street addict-user resorts to heroin because he is a "neurotic individual unable to cope with life's difficulties."[11] That is, with heroin he can shut out the depressing and unpleasant facts of living in a slum and the perhaps even more painful awareness that he has little if any real chance of escaping it. Or, if he is a middle-class user, he simply can turn off from whatever personal or social situation he is unable or unwilling to face. Put more baldly, this is the character-defect theory of addiction.

(But even assuming these to be the chief reasons for addiction—an assumption which, as we shall see below, is probably invalid—I can't quite bring myself to believe them neurotic responses. In one sense heroin is a realistic solution to the problems an individual faces in the ghettos. Not many ghetto dwellers escape the ghetto. Not many talented ghetto dwellers escape the ghetto. Understanding the actual prospects and understanding the fact that heroin is a psychic as well as physical pain reliever, I feel that using it to turn off from present pain and future futility is not neurotic.)

Given the fact that the majority of our addict-users are from minority groups, it is not surprising that the character-defect theory is widely held. Most of what we learn about the heroin user comes from the reports of the police, physicians, psychiatrists, and social workers. As a group they are essentially middle- and upper-middle class, operating under a value system quite different from that held in the urban ghetto, and they naturally tend to judge the typical heroin user by psychological and social norms appropriate to the white middle-class but inappropriate in a different culture.[12] Thus we are given the picture of a man becoming an addict-user because he is a person crippled by basic character defects, a person who is immoral, unintelligent and consequently unable to face the problems of life. Underlying this assessment, perhaps informing it, is a stance of moral superiority which assumes that anyone with sufficient "character" can resist the dangerous pleasures of addictive drugs. This stance, in addition to ignoring the basic pharmacology of heroin, also ignores the number of people with presumedly strong characters—doctors, clergymen, lawyers, teachers, etc.— who have become addicted to morphine after hospital treatment and have found that strength of character didn't help them at all. And strength or weakness of character is not considered an appropriate factor in the analysis of laboratory animals tested with morphine and heroin. Nevertheless, they are easily made addicts.

The character-defect theory of drug addiction, as Dr. Marie Nyswander has pointed out, does have a superficial plausibility:

> One of the more telling arguments in favor of the . . . "character defect" theory of addiction is the addict's antisocial behavior and attitude. It is a strong argument. Drug-hungry addicts are, indeed, self-centered and indifferent to the interests of others. They are irresponsible, thieves, and liars. And they commit crimes.

But, as she points out, ". . . these things are true only because addicts need drugs; they are the results of addiction, not causes." Moreover, as she so rightly states,

> We have yet to see a study that tells anything about the addictive personality except to describe an addict *while he is an addict*. Nor have studies made clear why certain persons in a population exposed to narcotics become addicts and not others. It is quite possible that the initial impulse in most is a combination of curiosity and opportunity, and that some metabolic quirk leads some of the experimenters on to true addiction. The patients themselves cannot explain it. In one patient's words:

> "Nobody knows *why* he goes on drugs. Everybody can tell you *how*. 'They' say it's because of the environment, being from a poverty-stricken area, or being brought up in a broken home, or things like that. But there are people with the same problems who don't take drugs, and there are people from good homes, wealthy homes, not broken homes, and they do take drugs. Maybe it's all in the head, as 'they' say. But I don't remember having any psychological drive to take drugs. It's just that you're going with a crowd, and they're all taking drugs, and you want to be 'in,' so you try it."[13]

And finally, as Dr. Nyswander and others have made clear,

> if . . . there is some basic character defect or personality pattern that leads to addiction or makes a person especially susceptible to addiction, then we would expect to find some specific "drug-addict personality pattern" among our patients. None has emerged. Their range of personal characteristics is as varied as in any other group of the same number of individuals.[14]

The simple truth is that at the present time we do not know why one person finds heroin pleasant and becomes a user and another does not. There is even less data available on why, out of a group of experimenters with the same cultural and economic backgrounds, only a small percentage will like the experience enough to go on to steady use. It has been suggested that a difference in metabolism distinguishes the one class from the other. If this proves to be the case, heroin addiction will be analogous to alcoholism in this respect.

Free samples used to hook potential customers, one shot leading inexorably to addiction, and the character-defect theory are all myths either lacking any foundation or supported by but the flimsiest of foundations. Nevertheless, they remain with us, as does another myth perhaps even further removed from any factual basis: marijuana leads to heroin. In polite, semi-scientific circles this myth is given respectability by a name—the steppingstone theory.

The steppingstone theory has an interesting history. In hearings on what was to become the Marijuana Tax Act of 1937—an act which owes its birth to the Bureau of Narcotics' intensive propaganda campaign depicting marijuana as the direct cause of a wide variety and amount of violent crime—Harry Anslinger in his testimony replied to the question "whether the marijuana addict graduates into a heroin . . . user" by saying

> No, sir; I have not heard a case of that kind. I think it is an entirely different class. The marijuana addict does not go in that direction.[15]

But after achieving his aim of criminalizing the marijuana user, and after becoming increasingly interested in heroin traffic and use, Mr. Anslinger had a somewhat different story to tell. Testifying in 1955 before the Daniel Subcommittee on Improvements in the Federal Criminal Code of the Committee of the Judiciary, he played down marijuana, explaining that the Bureau's various statistics and charts on addiction ignored the marijuana addict "because he is not a true addict." The real menace was the heroin addict. Senator Daniel, after so many years of hearing about the marijuana menace, was not so ready to ignore it. He asked Anslinger a question: "Now . . . while we are discussing marijuana, the real danger there is that the use of marijuana leads many people eventually to the use of heroin and the drugs that do cause complete addiction: is that true?" Mr. Anslinger didn't abandon his long-time commitment to fully cooperating with Congressional bodies. He replied, "That is the great problem and our great concern about the use of marijuana, that eventually if used over a long period, it does lead to heroin addiction."[16]

As does, for example, the use of barbiturates, alcohol, tobacco or milk, if you are willing to believe that the use of any substance is a direct causative factor in the subsequent use of any other substance. Or if the point you wish to make is more important to you than the truth.

The United States Task Force Report of 1967 laid the marijuana-to-heroin myth to rest:

> The charge that marijuana "leads to the use of addictive drugs" needs to be critically examined. There is evidence that a majority of heroin users who come to the attention of public authorities have, in fact, had some prior experience with marijuana. But this does not mean that one leads to the other in the sense that marijuana has an intrinsic quality that creates a heroin liability. There are too many marijuana users who do not graduate to heroin, and too many heroin addicts with no prior marijuana use, to support such a theory. *Moreover there is no scientific basis for such a theory.*[17] (italics added)

Laid it to rest but did not kill it. The myth still lingers

on, though not usually formulated in Anslinger's simple way. Some examples:

1 "While pot use doesn't 'lead' to the use of more dangerous drugs, it is not totally innocent, because the use of one pleasurable drug may reinforce the user's tendency to employ other drugs."[18]

2 "Escalation between cannabis and opiates certainly does occur ... Those in whom this takes place probably are those mentally unstable individuals who have a predisposition to use drugs and would tend to find satisfaction and an acceptable form of release from their cares and stresses as a consequence of taking a variety of centrally acting drugs.[19] Edward R. Bloomquist, the disingenuous author of (1) above, introduces (3) below by saying that "Although the steppingstone theory is not valid per se, it is a fact, however, that certain aspects of marijuana use do encourage (but do not force or lead the user to try) the use of more dangerous drugs. Surveying 75,000 university students, Doris Milman found the following situation:"[20]

3 "Marijuana was the first illicit drug used and the most widely used illicit drug being employed by more than 80 percent of drug users; also two thirds of drug users employed more than one drug. These facts, taken together ... lead inescapably to the conclusion that marijuana is the first step in the direction of drug abuse."[21]

4 "In a recent study of adolescent offenders in New York, the likelihood of future heroin addiction as a factor of adolescent marijuana use was investigated. The results were conclusive.

LATER HEROIN USE BY ADOLESCENT OFFENDERS

DRUG USED—1962	% USING HEROIN 1963-67
Marijuana	41.3
Heroin	52.5
None	15.1

Source: Inciardi, 'Later Heroin Use by Adolescent Marijuana and Heroin Users and by Non-Drug Using Adolescent Offenders,' September 1968. at 4, table 1 (study on file at N.Y.S. Narcotic Comm'n. Research Dep't.).

"Thus, while few non-drug-using adolescent offenders progress to heroin addiction . . . a large proportion [of marijuana users] had "graduated" to heroin use within five years. The authors of the report believed that the data were strong enough to warrant the conclusion that, for adolescent delinquents, 'marijuana use is almost as portentous of adult heroin use as is actual use of heroin as an adolescent.' "[22]

I have arranged these restatements of the steppingstone theory in order of ascending greater plausibility; from the squishy generality and the invalid assumption to the spurious conclusion drawn from what is presumedly accurate data. When pressed to prove the flat assertion that marijuana leads to heroin, the steppingstone advocates have usually proceeded along this route, citing statistical studies which reputedly link the incidence of marijuana use to the incidence of heroin use. They would be better off sticking with the all-encompassing vagueness of Bloomquist (1), which admirably resists complete refutation. And certainly it would be more honest to do so. For at bottom what they are doing is advocating a *belief*, a belief they hold in face of all the evidence available. Better then to admit one's naked beliefs than to attempt clothing them in easily-removed statistical garb.

Example (1) is so vague and so wide in scope that it is hard to imagine what evidence its author would accept as conclusive against it. When you use constructions like "such and such *may reinforce* such and such," you are always in the position of being able to say "true, but it *may*. We must await further evidence." Moreover, this example appears grounded in a truth of human experience: pleasure reinforces our willingness to seek further pleasure. Appears grounded, but in fact is not, as it would be if there were any reason to believe that the average marijuana user sees heroin as a possible future pleasure. As far as anyone has been able to determine, they do not. There is, however, one way in which the pleasures found in marijuana may lead to trying to find pleasure in heroin: after many years of hearing marijuana depicted by the authorities as a dangerous drug and then finding from personal experience that it is not, some young people have tried heroin on the rationale that if "they" lied about marijuana, "they" are probably lying about heroin. Quite clearly this occasional progression is not caused by marijuana, but rather by official untruths about marijuana. But to get a full appreciation of example (1)'s lack of content, we should translate it into terms appropriate to Victorian moral theology: indulging in the pleasures of masturbation may reinforce one's tendency to commit rape.

Example (2) is built solely on a 'fact' for which no investigator has found objective evidence: that there is some mental instability or character defect which leads to heroin use.

Example (4) is essentially (3) dressed in different numbers and is invalid for the same reasons. But though its conclusion—"marijuana use is almost as portentous of adult heroin use as is actual use of heroin as an adolescent"—is meaningless respecting any causal link between marijuana and heroin for adolescent delinquents and completely unwarranted if applied to the general population, it does point to an important fact: namely that where heroin is an integral part of a culture, as it is in a big city ghetto and as it was for the large majority of the youths in this study, the chances of becoming a user are greatly increased. You can't become a heroin user unless heroin is available. The same goes for marijuana. Where either are widely available and widely used, your chances and willingness to try them are naturally greater than when they are not. It is not surprising, therefore, that most ghetto heroin users first used marijuana. They were introduced to it by friends in the same way they were later introduced to heroin. And, it should be added, in the same way they were introduced to tobacco and alcohol, both of which have a higher prior incidence of use among heroin addicts than marijuana.[23]

There are other myths associated with heroin, and some of them will be examined in later chapters, but one widely-held misconception should be cleared up before we go any further. For just as it is not uncommon to hear welfare recipients referred to as lazy or stupid, or both, it is also not uncommon to hear heroin users characterized in a like manner. This may have something to do with the fact that heroin users and welfare recipients are sometimes the same people—in New York there are a known 32,000 addicts on welfare[24]—but essentially the misconception stems from an inability to understand alien life-styles. In short, ignorance. And of course any number of prejudices. We see a black with no regular employment shooting drugs and getting high. Getting high, not working and being black are not positive acts or attributes in the majority culture. A liberal white will excuse a man for being black, but not holding a regular job is a sure sign of laziness. And given the legal, social and personal penalties incurred, the life of an addict is not that which an intelligent man would choose. Therefore addicts are stupid, a notion often reinforced by addicts themselves. They frequently refer to their condition as stupid or foolish.

Nevertheless, anyone much in contact with addicts is usually impressed by the intelligence they display. My own experience with addicts completely changed my folk-beliefs in this regard. I kept wondering why the majority of those with whom I came in contact showed a degree of intelligence and insight decidedly superior to that of the general run of people one meets. This thoroughly subjective evaluation is substantiated by one of the few modern studies made of addict intelligence.

During the early stages of his development of methadone therapy, Dr. Vincent Dole gave I.Q. tests to the addicts in the program. He found that his patients were underrepresented in the low ranges and consistently high in the superior ranges.[25] Dr. Dole makes it clear that he tested only a small group, but he also says that nothing he later learned put the findings in doubt.

> Now there are two possibilities to explain this. One is, which I was inclined to think of at first, and that was that they were smart to come to us [the early research program on methadone] ... But it works out that that isn't the answer. I think the other possibility is the correct one. You might call it the slow-rabbit theory. That is, that it's a very, very hard thing to be an addict. A person has to be pretty energetic, and pretty smart to hustle this much—to steal this much, to keep alive to be an addict. It's a hard job. It's like the slow rabbit in the woods. There aren't slow rabbits because they get eaten up. The fast rabbits that survive are

like the smart addicts ... If we say we've got 150,000 addicts in New York City, we might say to ourselves we've got a 100,000 pretty smart people.[26]

As Dr. Dole says, a person has to be pretty energetic and pretty smart to hustle enough to take care of a heroin habit. And just as I have been impressed by the intelligence of the addicts I've met, I have been equally impressed by their energy. When not on the nod or when not sick from lack of heroin, they take care of the business of their lives—getting heroin—with incredible industry. This fact has led some investigators to believe that perhaps one causative factor in addiction is that it meets "the basic human need of activity directed toward realizable goals by engaging in a continuous pursuit of drugs, which itself becomes an activity with its own sense of accomplishment and its own self-contained goals."[27] Similarly, a study done in British Columbia in 1956 suggests that the typical street addict is an industrious person for whom addiction provides the only available ambition-satisfying career.[28]

To most readers the notion that heroin can offer an ambition-satisfying career, let alone the *only* ambition-satisfying career, will be hard to swallow. But if one takes the time to carefully consider how limited are the possibilities afforded an intelligent young black in an urban ghetto, the notion's implausibility rapidly diminishes.

All that has been said so far in this chapter may be viewed as an attempt to discourage stereotypic thinking about heroin addiction. As Marie Nyswander has said of addicts, "their range of personal characteristics is as varied as in any other group of the same number of individuals."[29] Put another way, apart from patterns common to anyone leading an illegal, addicted life, there is no stereotype junkie. But even if the reader comes to believe this, it

73

will be hard to erase the picture of a young, black, urban ghetto male as *the* junkie. And to be sure, in New York City 43.9 percent of the heroin users listed on the Narcotics Register are black and another 21.8 percent are Puerto Rican, and the large majority of both classes are poor, male, and young. Moreover, the 32.2 percent who are white are also predominantly poor, young males. Still, just as prior to the Harrison Narcotics Act of 1914 most opiate users were white and middle or upper class, there is now a growing class of white middle- and upper-class heroin users. How many there are, no one really knows, but in the last two or three years there have been an increasing number of heroin o.d.'s reported in the affluent suburbs, and heroin is now readily available in the schools of these areas.

Of course there have always been affluent heroin users. Their money, white skin and social class help keep them from police surveillance, and consequently their numbers are under-reported. It may help to broaden our view of the heroin world, help us graduate from stereotype thinking, if we listen to the story of a white, college-educated, former addict. More important in this respect, perhaps, is that his introduction to heroin and at least part of his experience with it, could just as well be the story of an East Harlem junkie.

The tape of the following transcript was recorded in February 9, 1972.

* * *

My Confessions: I first used heroin in 1962. I was with a bunch of people I had met initially when I was eighteen. We were all still in high school, me in Queens and all of them in Brooklyn. We became friends because we were all into radical, Jewish circle-type things. They turned me on to grass—in Prospect Park.

At that time, grass was such a quiet thing that I couldn't even tell my closest friends in my own school that I was using grass. One had self-preservation instincts.

It was a very close kind of fellowship, the grass fellowship, and it had links with black kids, which was kind of nice. I remember meeting people from Harlem, through scoring grass, and going to their houses on a kind of close basis, back and forth. The same people began using heroin after they had all left home and were into different colleges around the city or just working at jobs. That was in 1962 too. My feeling about that period was that we were just trying every drug there was, more or less. We'd been lied to about grass, and therefore we couldn't accept anybody's word about anything else. What I really mean is that the lies we had been handed, and the resulting disbelief on our part after we had tried grass, led us to experimenting. You couldn't help feeling you had to find out for yourself if you were really going to see what drugs were about.

The first time I actually came into contact with heroin was when I met this street poet—whose name I can't remember—an older guy who got sent over to my house by another friend with a note pinned on him: "Help This Person." He had to crash; you see, he'd been up for nights on amphetamines and needed a place to sleep. So there he was in my home. And he was a real person, a dedicated, crazy, flipped-out forty-year-old street poet. Been in the Navy, among other things. Anyway, this guy was mostly into amphetamines, but he used junk too. The whole thing was using the needle, that was the crossover line—whether you were into using a needle or not.

I remember the first time I shot junk, somebody helped me with all the paraphernalia, especially the needle. There was a whole lot of expertise, elitism involved. That was the feeling anyway. A status thing. That first experience shooting, it was like white snow falling. Extremely peaceful. And I remember thinking—this is what they're talking about. It was an almost religious feeling, a unity of mind and body. There definitely were religious connotations. Funny, it was spiritual, but at the same time very physical in the sense of sexual body feelings. That whole thing of total body orgasm was there for me. Of course I'm abstracting the pleasant from the unpleasant. There was that something that made you go towards it, want to keep taking it even before you had a habit. I wrote a poem one time which describes the feeling ... but that's another story.

But what happened to me was that even though I had this very nice experience, experiences, with junk, it started to seem totalitarian to me. I could see that junk was a totalitarian, fascist drug. It reduced your freedom and controlled your life. I was still using it, though, because I figured I could keep from being hooked. And I didn't have a habit, I was just using it every once in a while. My friends, the ones from high school, were into it pretty heavy, and they would come over to my house every so often and I'd turn on with them. That was in the summer of '62.

Eventually the apartment got to be a place where a lot of people would come and hang out. People would cop on the street using the old balloon method, the idea being that if you got busted you could swallow it and retrieve it later. Then they'd come back to the apartment and shoot up.

The life I saw at that time began turning me off. Very much. Just what people were into. Like F.T., an underground filmmaker now, was sixteen then, and she and a girlfriend of hers got into turning weird, sleazy tricks to get money for junk. In one sense what they were all doing was a way of getting out into the world. I mean, if you've lived your life without having to make money, and then all of a sudden you have to make a lot of money, your life quickly becomes a lot less sheltered. It changes very considerably.

And it always seemed to me that for many people junk gave a structure to lives that had no structure. A very fully structured life. Rituals, alliances being formed, money being made, excitement. Excitement for sure, a chase with a reward at the end. Meet back at the house. Did you cop? Did *you* cop? No. No. Yeah. Oh wow! Then the dividing up of the sacrament, with the older, most experienced junkie with the biggest habit and the most knowledge, taking the most. Anyhow, watching it all and seeing what a drag it was sort of turned me off to the whole scene. I was living with a woman at the time, and she had started shooting with me. We'd been on a junk run for about a week, and I was beginning to feel that if I kept it up I'd become addicted, and that wasn't a good thing. I didn't feel that using the drug itself was necessarily bad, but the addiction was certainly bad. Anyway, she woke up one morning with a cold and said she wanted some junk because that would clear up her cold—and in fact it does seem to help. But I said no, I don't think that's a good idea—we've been using so much, we should stop now. She got very upset; began to cry and everything, saying you can't tell me what to do, it's O.K., I'm not using much, and etc.

Well, when I saw all that going down, I said *yes, this is* the time to stop. I mean her reaction was all out of proportion to what had happened. So we split the city. Went out and stayed with her parents in New Jersey. Stopped the junk completely. In terms of withdrawal I had

77

a couple of days comparable to a very bad cold or the flu.

Then I went back to school that fall, and by that time people at school were beginning to use junk. Some people at Harvard. Just a few, but a couple of my friends ended up addicted. Two of my good friends.

When I came back to the city in '64, I got in with a bunch of people who were shooting up. Speed and junk. And some of the people from the earlier days were beginning to have serious trouble with their lives. One guy o.d.'d in his apartment. The police came and saved him with oxygen, but it was very close. And other people I had known had o.d.'d. And a girl who had been playing around, not actually turning tricks, but posing for old men in those seamy photography joints, had become a prostitute and completely hooked. And so on.

But it still seemed to me something you could keep under control if you wanted to. I mean, it seemed so obvious that you had to really *want* to get addicted. The idea some people have, that if you take one shot you're addicted, is so ridiculous. As far as I could tell, it took about two weeks of steady shooting to get to the point, not where you couldn't stop, but where you really dug it and felt a craving for it. And considering all the things you have to do to use junk, getting hooked just has to be a very conscious act. Scoring, cooking, tying up, preparing the needles, shooting. It's an act with a lot of scenes. It's nothing done casually, you have to work at it to become an addict.

Of course some people get hooked on the rituals. They make a whole way of life just out of the rituals. And then there's the needle freaks. Christ . . . Funny, no one talked much about it, but there would be people that even when there was no junk or so little as to be nothing, would go through the whole shooting process. They'd get off watching the blood go up into the syringe. Something like sexual perversion there, I think. I mean, the way they'd flex their muscles so the blood came into the syringe very strongly, so that they knew they'd made a hit rather than missed a vein. Then the inevitable 'oohs and ahhs' as the blood rose. And then the way some people would dig pushing the needle in and out three or four times "to make sure it was all in." Definitely sexual connotations.

Getting back to me. I was out of school, and the Army wanted me. And for various reasons I decided to become a real junkie for a period prior to my physical. I guess it was because I wanted to be able to honestly say I was a junkie and get deferred. I knew I couldn't lie to them about it, because I can't do that kind of thing very well. And I wasn't into going to jail as a resistance hero. I figured being a junkie was the safest and surest way out. Of course this wasn't the whole story. It was my rationalization. The one thing I'm sure of, though, is that there was something in me that really wanted to come to terms with an area of my life completely. In this case, junk.

But I couldn't really afford to be a full-on junkie, and since I wasn't into being a thief, the way I managed the economics of junk was to score for other people and then shoot up with them. That went on for about two weeks. Filled myself with junk.

I went down to the Whitehall Induction Center for my physical after using a combination of amphetamines and heroin. It had the amazing effect of, when I had to talk, the speed would come on and give the boost I needed and when I had to wait in those endless lines, I could switch to nodding.

I had answered affirmative to taking drugs on the card you fill out, and they took me to the psychiatrist. He asked me if I ever took acid. I said yes, and he asked me to describe its effects. So I described a kind of terrible deity vision I once had, a vision of a centipede devouring itself—actually clouds turning into centipedes. Well as soon as I put that into his head he said, "That's enough!"

Then he asked to see my arms and determined from them that I'd been a junkie for years. Which wasn't really so dumb on his part, come to think of it. I'd been shooting speed for some time, and for the two-week period I was shooting junk many times a day. Anyway, he told me I was 4-F.

They then sent me to a social worker who supposedly was connected to the city. She wanted me to go on a rehabilitation program, but my feeling was that they would rehabilitate you into the Army. So I told her I would kick junk myself, that I had met a woman I was in love with, and therefore I could stop using drugs. And as I got into the story—which was true to a degree, but still a very soap-opera scenario—it took on magical dimensions. I could see myself kicking junk for the love of a woman. It really appealed to me.

After I left the place, I stopped at a friend's house and told them it had worked out, I was out and not in. Then I phoned my mother and told her. Then I went home to the woman I was in love with, and we went out to get something to eat. And sitting there in the restaurant, I burst into tears. From the total experience, I think. Seeing everybody being literally sent off to war. It was very strong in my mind: the processing thing that everybody had gone through, was going to go through in the future, and that I had managed to remove myself from. When you look at it stoned like I was, it takes on mythic dimensions. Which in fact it has. People going through like sheep. It all seemed very terrible to me. It is terrible.

(I should say that one or two years later I would have

had a lot of trouble getting out the way I did. They'd gotten wise to the drug act. But at that time there was still the idea that drugs were something extraordinary, so I had no trouble.)

Anyway, I never used anything after that. When some junkie friends—and I didn't drop my junkie friends—came over to the house, I asked if anyone wanted a set of works. Naturally someone did, and I gave them all the works I had around the house. I was completely finished with junk.

It seemed to me that what I had done, psychologically, was to create a scenario for myself that allowed me to give up junk. At least it served that purpose for me. And very well. Even the withdrawal was inconsequential in terms of any real physical or mental suffering.

Unless you are a rich junkie who can pay someone else to get it, your life is completely taken up with scoring junk. And taken up with everything else that goes along with being a criminal. That's why I think junk is totalitarian. Not because of the drug itself, but because of its illegality.

With me, I just constructed a way out. Most of the people I was into it with got out too. Of course some didn't.

* * *

With Alice Through the Looking Glass

The reader will have noticed by now that the term "user" rather than the term "addict" is often employed, and frequently the term "addict-user" when speaking of the whole population of heroin users. This is not done in adherence to the stylistic canon which finds variety preferable to consistency, but rather because the different terms reflect factual distinctions usually overlooked. Contrary to the BNDD—whose Dr. Greenwood, in his study on the size of the addict population, wrote, "Our major assumption is that everyone who is known as an addict to a law enforcement agency, and then reported as such to the BNDD . . . is indeed an addict."[1] —not every user of heroin, and consequently not every person arrested for possession, is an addict. It is commonly said that to be truly addicted to heroin, two factors must be present: *tolerance,* which develops when response to the same dose of a drug decreases with repeated use; and *physical dependence,* which is a "physiological state of adaptation to a drug . . . following the development of tolerance, which results in a characteristic set of withdrawal symptoms . . . when administration of the drug is stopped."[2] But clearly physical dependence cannot be a sufficient condition for addiction. If it were, addiction would be relatively easy to cure. We would need only incarcerate an addict until his system was purged of heroin. And the revolving doors of our treatment facilities and jails are ample proof that physical dependence is not all there is to addiction.

There is a third factor, perhaps the most important one, and that is *craving.*[3] Craving, in the sense used here, involves (1) an abnormal intensity of desire for heroin, (2) an abnormal reaction to any failure to fulfill the desire for heroin (e.g., taking actions to get heroin without any regard for the consequences), and (3) an abnormal limitation on modifying the desire for heroin (e.g., an unwilling-ness to accept a substitute). The junkie who will rob his already poor family, sell his wife or break a store window in broad daylight is a junkie in the grip of craving.

Why craving develops in some users and not in others is not clearly understood. One study of adolescent addicts showed, however, that the condition necessary for the development of craving is a high level of distress. For example, they found there were many users who had been taking heroin for some time without any signs of craving until a psychosexual crisis occurred. With the "need for relief from anxiety verging on panic, their craving began."[4] Heroin of course affords great relief from distress.

But this development of craving among heroin users suddenly placed in a stress situation is not universal. Some develop it, others do not. The chief obstacle in finding why this is so seems to be, as Marie Nyswander has pointed out, that all studies of addicts take place *after* they become addicted. And "since there are marked difficulties of communication with . . . addicts, we do not learn easily about the level of emotional distress as a factor . . ."[5] Furthermore, even among users who crave heroin, the level of craving is not constant, nor is it highly correlated with the level of physical dependence.[6]

From what has been said so far, it should be clear that addiction is not simply the result of using heroin or even the result of becoming physically dependent on it; and that craving, a necessary condition of true addiction, is a very complicated phenomenon, affecting different persons for different reasons and even affecting the same person differently at different times. Classifying all users as addicts, therefore, is not only a mistake, but gives the illusion that some universal panacea for addiction can be found. With so many different factors involved, no one therapy or treatment can be expected to work for all.

Even among regular users there are clearly defined types. There are those, for example, who, though they use regularly, use infrequently enough that tolerance does not develop, and hence no physical dependence develops. Those people are usually week-end users. Joy-poppers. Many of them eventually slip out of the week-end class and become daily users. But many of them use heroin "for several years on a more-or-less regular week-end basis and then, apparently without difficulty, quit."[7] Such users are not and never were addicts.

And addiction is not the only basic difference between the occasional or regular week-end user and the daily user. Unlike the daily user, who is almost always an addict, the week-ender has no pressing need to acquire large amounts of money to supply a habit, and thus does not have to become totally involved in the heroin scene. Such a user must neither modify his other interests nor radically change his life-style in order to meet his need for heroin. And being in all important social aspects indistinguishable from the typical members of the community in which he lives, he does not often come to the attention of the legal authorities.

Further confounding the common notion that all users are addicts is the existence of persons who use heroin on a daily basis for periods of time without either developing physical dependence or craving and who are able to stop using with little effort. Some of the best-informed researchers in the field doubt the existence of such types. Nevertheless, they do exist. They are a rare breed, given the properties of heroin, but a breed worth investigating, if only because they offer us a glimpse of heroin use as far removed from the stereotype as possible, while at the same time they exhibit patterns—in their initiation to the drug, their feelings about it and at least in part of their life-styles—common to most addicts. More important, we should investigate them because we don't know *why* they are able to resist dependence and addiction, and we *should* know why. Perhaps the reason is that, as the speaker who closed the last chapter stated, you have to really *want* to become addicted, and these people *don't* want that. Or perhaps their metabolisms differ from those of addicts. Certainly this is a question science should study, for the correct answer might go far in helping establish the true causes of addiction. Such a study has not yet been done, and what follows is only a biographical sketch of such a person. Hopefully it will stimulate someone with the proper credentials to look deeper into the matter.

Alice is twenty-nine and white and pretty. She teaches grade school in Harlem. Her students like her very much. She has used heroin on a regular basis for short periods of time. She still uses it occasionally. She says, and the few of her friends that I have met agree, that she has never been addicted.

A tape transcript is a poor vehicle in which to display a personality. One loses the nuances expressed in the inflections of a singular voice. And Alice's voice is very singular, an instrument which perfectly reflects her vivacious character. All her many shadings of meaning, especially her ironies, are lost in the transcript. What remains is a shadow of Alice, but a shadow filled with information.[8]

When did you first take . . .
Alice: My first taste?
Drugs, period. Like when did you have your first drink?
Alice: I never drank really, but I think I was nineteen, and
somebody got me stoned on champagne, and . . .

. . . it was all downhill from there.

Alice: Yes . . . Four of us had seven or eight bottles, and I just said to myself, Alice, that's not where it's at—so I never drank again. I never did anything really.

Where are you from? Are you . . . oh, you're from New York! Where else could you be from . . . So you were nineteen and you were in school?

Alice: Yes.

What school?

Alice: City College . . . I mean I might have had a drink before that, but my first real bombed-out drunk was then when I was nineteen.

And you graduated. You became, you are a teacher.

Alice: Yeah, I graduated to hard stuff.

And you got a credential too. Was this all in one go?

Alice: No. It took me five years and two summer schools. I went three years in the day, two at night, and two summer schools. I got my B.A. when I was twenty-two and my teaching credential when I was twenty-three.

And when did you first smoke grass?

Alice: I don't remember . . . oh, when I was twenty-one or twenty-two. Yes, I was around twenty-one. Everybody I knew was into grass, and I never took anything. I was high on me. I just didn't take *anything*. Funny, I thought of grass the way people think of heroin and coke today. But then everyone was doing it, doing it, and I finally took my first drag or whatever. But I really didn't get into it then, because the people I first knew who were into it . . . well, I didn't respect them.

They weren't who you wanted to be.

Alice: Not at all. They were Peppermint Loungers. They were all hookers and pushers, and I was innocent Alice. And really, the whole trip down there: I loved seeing it and being there, but I didn't want to *be* it. But then

when these really heavy, groovy creative cats, and
people into rock music, when they started to turn me
on, it was a different thing. I did it and I liked it. I
started smoking grass and I smoked for years. And for
years that's all I did. No other drugs.

What was the next thing you were introduced to?

Alice: Coke. I took coke before I took acid.

How old were you?

Alice: About twenty-six or twenty-seven . . . let's see, yes,
twenty-six. I used to do it . . . say, once a month I'd
have a few snorts.

You were very moderate.

Alice: Yes, always. Like my mother says: moderation,
everything in moderation. So I took my scag in moderation, my coke in moderation . . . no excesses. Except on
special occasions.

And the next thing you touched, touched you?

Alice: Oh, acid.

Acid before you took junk?

Alice: Oh, yes. I just had junk the first time last . . . a year
and a half ago.

*Your friend Terence, the one you told me about yester-
day, he was into junk?*

Alice: Yeah, he was into it, all right. And I was over at his
place, and there was this chick there. I was about to
leave, I hardly knew either of them, and they started to
get the needles out and I thought, oh, my God. And it
was the chick who said, come on, we'll just jab you in
the ass. I said, wait, wait just a second; and then I said
to myself, well, I've got to experience everything in
life—I'd never even snorted it or anything—and why not
this? So they jabbed my ass, and I nodded, wow, did I
·nod. I just completely sat back and . . . it was like
tripping.

You didn't get sick?

Alice: No, not that time. Sometimes you get deathly ill and sometimes you get beautifully high right off.

The first time I got mainlined I really got sick.

Alice: You shot it?

Twice. This fellow I met doing the book skin-popped me one day, and the next day he gave me two mainlines.

Alice: For what? Just for an experience?

Well, yes. I was writing a book on heroin and . . .

Alice: Excuses, excuses.

No. I felt uneasy, that's all. I can't really justify it. It's simply that I didn't feel right, doing the book and not having tried it. As it turned out, it didn't help me much. I still don't know what it's really like to like heroin, because I didn't like it. It was just an unpleasant downer for me.

Now it's not just a downer for you.

Alice: Well . . .

You liked that first skin-pop.

Alice: And that was really heavy. I mean, it really took over. I guess I loved it . . . oh, hell, I *do* love it.

You said it was like tripping.

Alice: Yeah. You hallucinate on it. When you close your eyes you completely hallucinate.

Shortchanged again. I mean, I got over the initial sickness and felt very, very cool. I didn't give a damn about anything. I went for a walk, looked at the river. Couldn't get interested in the river. Went into a coffee shop and ordered coffee and a doughnut. They came and I couldn't get interested in them. I just didn't care.

Alice: I lost so much weight . . .

I remember picking up the coffee and finding it was scalding hot. So I put it down to cool. But I never could get interested in picking it up again. So I left and walked some more. I've never been that uninvolved, that removed

90

*in my life. I was the complete spectator. And I never
thought of closing my eyes. It never occurred to me that
maybe I would be seeing things. No one ever mentioned
that. And I never felt like closing my eyes.*

Alice: Well, it's a weird thing, because when you sit down
and close your eyes, you're in a completely different
head than when you open your eyes and stand up and
start doing things. When you're up and moving, you're
in a different head from minute to minute.

*Would you say that the closed-eye hallucinations are like
acid tripping? Closed-eye acid tripping?*

Alice: No, no, it's much . . . it's hard to describe. It's
almost like your mind is carried away. With acid you're
right in yourself, constantly moving inside yourself—but
these are hallucinations that come from left field.

One example.

Alice: Oh, just patterns . . .

You get that with acid.

Alice: But there's a different feeling behind seeing them.

*Ahhh . . . you're not as involved with them. You're a
spectator.*

Alice: Exactly. You don't go through any heavy head
trips. I find heroin gives me a different feeling every
time, but that's the basic feeling—complete detachment.
I mean, you aren't in any sense in control of it—you
aren't hallucinating on what you see, you're hallucinating on what you don't see. It just comes from out there
some place, and you have nothing to do with it, you're
just watching it. With acid, I think, you are very
involved with your hallucinations; with heroin it's just
the opposite . . . But very, very beautiful hallucinations.
I mean I can understand why junkies dig it so much:
there is *no* play on the mind. Nodding is really a nice
part of heroin. And the weird thing about the nod

is—well, we used to sometimes just shoot up and lay in bed and watch TV or something, or just lay there and talk and nod. And I realized that sometimes when I was nodding it was such a far out nod that I'd maybe picture myself walking in the street, and I'd see someone I knew walk by, and I'd say out loud to Terence, "Oh, there's so and so," thinking that we were actually there, when all the time except for the speaking I was in a nod. It happened several times, that thinking you were actually where you were nodding. I'd say something to Terence like, "Look at that car, I'd like that"—and I'd be in my bedroom.

What about the rush? A lot of junkies I've talked with speak about a tremendous sexual rush on heroin. I didn't get anything like that at all.

Alice: I got it. It depends on who you're with and what the circumstances are. But if the situation is right, then the sexual thing is intensified. Sex is.

Almost everyone I've talked to says that sex goes out the window. It's the last thing they're interested in.

Alice: Well, it's physically hard for a guy to have sex. But we were still into it, quite a bit. I can see where you wouldn't think about it, wouldn't need it. But I used to . . . I loved it when I was stoned. I guess maybe it's a matter of how long you had been on heroin and what your relationship was with somebody . . . After a while, though, it usually got to be nothing but a junk relationship, and that's it.

Well, this sexual rush thing—they weren't talking about sex with another person, they . . .

Alice: Not even with themselves.

They were talking about it feeling like an orgasm in their stomachs or a total body orgasm, as one guy said. In fact as about five guys said. Maybe they picked the idea up reading, because you read that too. I don't know.

Alice: I get very sexually aroused by shooting smack. Not so much as with coke, but I do get it. And the environment in which I shoot makes a big difference. The whole thing with the needle is very sexual.

The whole thing with the needle turns me off. I don't like needles. I start getting sick as soon as I see a needle. Which is maybe why I started feeling sick the moment the rush started.

Alice: After you've been doing it a while, the rush sort of mellows out. I mean you still get the rush and everything, but you sort of know what to expect. It's not a shock to you. It's something you're waiting for, and expecting, and it comes and that's it. It's not a matter of fearful expectation, for example. When you know what you're getting, it modifies your reactions. And the thing about the needle—well, Terence usually shot me up. Occasionally, if he couldn't hit a vein, someone else would do it. But he was always there. I never hit myself, which is probably significant. Once you start shooting yourself up, it's a whole different trip. But I dig the needle part of shooting junk. I *like* that. I really do. Like with Terence it was done with a sexual tone. Not overtly, but it was there.

It was attention. Direct personal attention.

Alice: Right. And very careful, very artistic. It's an art, or it can be.

Anyone who's had to get shots at a doctor's office knows it is an art, because most of them aren't artists. Most of them are plumbers.

Do you know many confirmed junkies?

Alice: (laughing hard) Well, take Terence. He just *loves* junk. That's his weakness in life—he loves junk. But he's a schizo, and being one he can turn himself off and on

93

to different trips just like *this* (snaps fingers). I mean, he's come off heroin by himself; for a long time he'll just stop. He's stopped after doing heavy, heavy doses. All of a sudden he'll just say, nah, and go on to something else. Other times, though, he fights it and keeps going back and back to junk. Maybe it depends on what personality he's in at the time.

What about your personality when you're on junk? Does it . . .

Alice: When you first go on junk, your personality çhanges *away* from you. Then when you've been on it a while, *that* becomes your personality, and when you're not on it, you're away from yourself. So after doing junk a while, what you are when you're on it is your normal personality. Junk then just brings you back to yourself, your junkie self.

(At this point, David, a friend of Alice's, came into the room.)

David: You want to hear about my little experience with heroin?

Sure. Why not?

David: Well, I did junk for the first time this year. I snorted it one time and really got zonked out. A real downer, not altogether pleasant. On balance I'd have to say it was an *un*pleasant experience. I didn't like being that zonked out, that down. On the other hand I could see the kind of dreamy buzz that started working on me. It was just something that cooled everying out, but on balance it cooled things out much too much. But I could see why some people dig it.

The first time I snorted I had scored some smack that was supposed to be good, but of course I couldn't tell. This fellow I got it from was always into good dope though. Had the very best cocaine. And he had this smack connection he said was good. So I tried it because I suppose I wanted to find out where it was at. Curiosity. I tried it for a couple of nights, but it just zonked me out much too much ... Ah, yes, then I smoked some much later. One more shot, give it another try, *that* old bag. And I got very sick, threw up a *lot*.

Alice: But you don't really mind throwing up when you're on junk!

David: I did.

Alice: Oh, I used to have a fear of throwing up, but I love throwing up on junk. It doesn't bother me at all, it's just not the same thing. It's a mechanical thing rather than an *involved* thing. It's relieving. We used to get into games when we threw up. Like we'd run into the bathroom together, throw up and say—"Families that throw up together, stay together." It's one of the things people do with all the weirdness of junk—make a game of it. There were times, though ... like I remember once when I was sick for three days after shooting. I was sick as hell. I mean I literally could hardly stand up. I'd ride in the car and have to stop every mile, open the door and throw up. That was horrible. But then most of the time it was beautiful, with no comedown even after the shot wore off. It's always different with me. Sometimes I get sick, sometimes I don't. But usually being nauseous while I was high never bothered me at all.

You once told me that Terence was a dealer. So he didn't have trouble getting heroin?

Alice: Even when you didn't want it, people would show up at the door with it. Like when he was trying to kick. That's what made him leave New York.

In a lot of ways your experience with heroin hasn't been the usual one.

Alice: Yeah, we never had to hustle. We never had to go

mugging or worry about our next fix. We always had a supply.

Then you were . . .

Alice: If you've got a perverted mind, you might say we were lucky.

I've been in pain, I've had stomach aches and head-aches, and I've come home sometimes like that, and the minute that needle goes in, I'm like *this*—it takes away everything. And the funny thing is,. with me, it never comes back. With some people, when the junk wears off, the illness comes back, only worse. Not with me. The junk wears off and I feel fine.

David: And it's funny how some people turn on to junk, like immediately, just right off. They skin-pop or snort or even mainline, and all of a sudden they're home. They're not addicts right then, but they *know* they've found what they've been looking for. I think they must feel a need, like I did in the hospital. It felt so good to get that pain out. I'm sure I got off on that morphine they gave me because I really needed it. But when I tried smack in the normal condition, it was mostly unpleasant. Probably because I had no need for it.

Alice: That's the way it was for you. It's not that way for everyone. I like smack when I'm feeling good in every way.

Did Terence deal heroin too?

Alice: Never here, but in England we did it. Actually we got into it because we went to score hash and nobody had any. And every time we went back to try and get hash, they'd say, "We don't have hash, but we have heroin." So finally these friends of ours who had ounces of heroin fronted some to us. And we knew a lot of people who were using it, regular junkies in Southamp-ton. We sold to them.

What were ounces selling for?

Alice: Well, a quarter ounce went for a hundred pounds, $250. And between $600 and $800 for an ounce. And it was always the same stuff, Chinese.

Chinese?

Alice: They called it Chinese. Probably it was *Indo*chinese. Anyway, it's completely different from the stuff here. Here it's white, there it's brown. And you always knew what you were getting. They don't cut it. Never cut it.

You were getting pure ounces? That's very unusual. In this country there is no way you are going to get a pure ounce. It's going to be cut at least twice. If you get a thirty percent ounce you're really doing well.

Alice: It's a very different scene in England. For one thing, they don't o.d., [They do. See Appendix A] because the stuff isn't cut . . . Say, you know what the worst thing in the world is? Methadone. *The worst shit out.*

Well . .

Alice: *The worst!* I could not *believe* where my mind was at. It took over. It absolutely took it over.

David: You shot it?

Alice: No, I drank it. It was wretched.

David: The thing with methadone, apparently, is that taking it orally you don't get high like you do shooting it.

Alice: Oh, I got *low*, baby.

David: When you shoot it, you supposedly get a rush, like on heroin.

Alice: Shooting it might get you a rush, but the head that endures after the rush is gone is complete zombieland. I mean, sure, some people take it; some people take anything.

Do you know people who have to hustle for their heroin?

Alice: All of them in Southampton. Everyone except us had to hustle.

What was their life like?

Alice: Well, here's what their schedule was—they had their bag in the morning because they scored it the night before. They'd wake up and shoot up so they could go out shoplifting. And they'd go shoplifting for a few hours a day. Then they'd find someone to sell the loot to, just make enough to score four or five bags—enough for the night and their shot in the morning. Then they'd spend the next day shoplifting again. And that was it.

David: What did they do on Sundays?

Alice: Sundays? Ahhh ... on Sundays they borrowed money from whoever shoplifted the cassette tape recorder instead of a coat. The stuff we were offered. I mean every day! Leather coats, cassette tape recorders, television sets—I mean, they used to walk out with television sets! They walked out with anything they could carry. They used to rip off drug stores for their stashes, but now no drugstores in the south will store more than a week's supply of drugs because, I think, they ripped off more than 200 or 300 chemists in one year all through England. The chemists got ripped off over and over again. Only up north do they still carry any big stashes in the chemists' shops. So now junkies strictly shoplift. All the junkies shoplift. It's a way of life.

Are there many busts?

Alice: They don't get busted for smack, they get busted for shoplifting. Everyone we knew in Southampton was busted for shoplifting at one time or another.

That reminds me—were you selling those one-grain bags in Southampton? And what were you selling them for?

Alice: That's where we sold them. Usually for between three and five dollars, depending on who and how much they bought, and whether we needed the bread or not at the moment.

And how many bags did you get out of an ounce?

Alice: Well, 250 packets out of the half-ounce, which came to a little less than a grain each ... [With ninety percent heroin, there would be 13,940 grains of pure heroin in a kilo, or 198 grains in a half-ounce] ... which was a nice size compared to what everyone else was selling. That's how we judged it, by what the other people were doing. But we only did that one half-ounce. That's all.

And how long did it take to sell that one half-ounce?

Alice: We didn't push it. We could have done it in a week, but we didn't always bother. We'd just let it lay there and not bother with it. Not even ourselves, because we weren't doing junk all the time then, and Terence wasn't hooked at the time. That's how he did get hooked again. We had it around all the time, and he just got back into it.

Do you know when Terence first got into heroin?

Alice: Just a few months before I did.

A lot of dealers seem to get into heroin ...

Alice: Sure, it comes their way. And they're so open to any drug. Coke comes, this comes, that comes, and they think they're on top of it and can handle anything because they're hip, cool dealers. Well, they can't. Terence got hooked in New York, which was why we left. And in England he was clean for three or four months. And I never thought ... Being the way I am I can take it or leave it. I can go without it for a week or a month or whatever. So I thought that once he was off it, he could stay off it. But he couldn't. He didn't try

99

hard enough. It's his weakness. Junk, that is.

Maybe "need" is a better word. You can't judge somebody else's need by your own. You can't get off junk by simply willing to get off. There has to be something informing that will, some change of situation that reduces the craving to a controllable level.

Alice: They can't possibly get off it staying in the same situation that got them into it, that's certain. You have to become almost a different person. It's impossible to get off and stay where you were.

Getting back to the business end—did you know many heroin dealers in London or Southampton?

Alice: In Southampton they had like one dealer in the whole town. Sometimes two or three people would come back with stuff, but basically there was one dealer. He would get up in the morning, go up to London—which is like an hour's train ride—score, and come back. Every day. And then he'd have a line of people waiting at his apartment for him to come back.

How many junkies do you think there were in Southampton?

Alice: Oh, wow . . .

Well, there was only one dealer, so how many could there be?

Alice: Oh, I meant there was one dealer I knew, like in the crowd that I knew. There were a lot of junkies in Southampton. I mean, it's not like New York or anything, but a lot for England. A lot of young people were getting into it when we were there. In the beginning, like we knew ten junkies. By the time we left, three or four months later, it had gone up to thirty or forty. People we knew. All the young kids we came across were starting in on it . . . [All the young kids *they* met. Heroin users attract heroin users.] . . . Like they

100

were shooting once or twice a week. Week-end junkies, which is the way they all start, it seems. The thing is, it was hard to get hash, which gave them a good excuse to try junk. They were just looking for excuses to get on it.

Do you think there's much to the idea that because heroin is such a powerful, dangerous drug, taking it is something of a status thing?

Alice: Yes, I certainly do. For the people who haven't done it, maybe it's not. The others, though, they say, well, I can try it. I can try anything ... And once you try it, it becomes an ego thing with you—bragging about how many bags you use a day. And they just dig the whole trip—getting the works, scoring the stuff, that's all their lives were. They lived to get stuff and do it up. It was a whole reason for living for them.

A meaningful activity.

Alice: Yeah, it gave them something to do. These people weren't educated, they didn't have money. They were sticking to Southampton because they were brought up there and they were afraid to go off on their own into the world. They just couldn't do that. The junk was an excuse to say there and have something to do. They had this local hangout, the place they'd all go to find out who was holding, and ask "Who's got?" They'd go anyway, I suppose. Junkies are very sociable. Even when they're nodding out in oblivion, they like to know there's someone else nodding out in oblivion near them. In a way it's part of the ritual of shooting in company. And they just love it. You know—get this together, that together, the water boiled, the spoon cleaned, the packets laid out, how much, me first, then you. It's a whole little ceremony and they get off on it.

A tea ceremony.

Alice: Yeah, except there's a reward. You get a rush.

101

By the way, what was the relationship between these people and the heroin clinics?

Alice: Well, none of them were registered. They avoided registration at all costs.

Do you know why?

Alice: Well, they knew the clinics try to rehabilitate you when you register, and they didn't want to be rehabilitated. They wanted to stay junkies. It was their life. Yet every one of them would say at one point, no more junk, we're going to get off. But they never did. Like, people would check themselves into hospitals to try and take the cure and they'd last about a week or two, and then they'd check out and go immediately to get a fix.

Did you know anyone who was getting heroin from a clinic?

Alice: Not really, but I have a feeling that a lot we knew are probably registered now, because the last month I was there they changed the law, and now it's very hard to get works. Before, you just walked in and said I want some works, and for seven cents you got your works over the counter. Then the government told the druggists they couldn't sell works without a prescription. So everybody started freaking out and borrowing cards of people who were registered. And people started saving their works. Funny, they had heroin all the time, but not works all the time. Which was a really bad thing, because they started borrowing, using each other's, and that's when you get hepatitis and all the rest. So I think a lot will register to get the works, never mind the heroin.

I've never talked to anyone who was on the program.

Alice: Well, they changed the program. Now seventy-five percent of the people on programs in England are getting methadone instead of heroin, and it does not do the same thing for you, baby. Which is another reason a lot of them are reluctant to register. The chances are they'll be given methadone or someone will try and rehabilitate them, and most of them I knew didn't want either. And then they are afraid if they register, the police at some point will come along and say they *have* to go into a clinic. So they feel it's best not to have your name linked with it at all.

Have you ever come across anyone like yourself, who used junk fairly regularly and didn't become addicted?

Alice: No. I'm sure there are, though. But not many. I met people who were doing it a lot more than I was. A lot more ... Oh, I was wrong, I *did* meet one cat there, a young guy, who'd been doing junk for years, and as soon as he'd see himself wanting to do it more than occasionally, he'd cool it. He was only twenty-one when I met him, and he'd been using it since he was seventeen. But he was a high, sensitive kid who read a lot. Not like the Southampton kids, who could hardly read a comic book. He had a lot more going for him and seemed to be able to handle junk very well. Those other kids had nothing else *but* junk.

By the way, did you or have you ever gotten to the point where you thought you might become addicted?

Alice: One time in England I did. I'd been doing it two or three times a week and then I did it a few days in a row, and I was really looking forward to doing it again. It wasn't any strong desire, but it *was* looking forward to the next fix. I guess there had to be a slight wanting involved. Anyway, that's when I said wait a minute! And I went for two weeks without using any.

Apart from Terence being hooked, and whatever that entailed for you, what was bad about heroin for you personally? Or was there anything bad in it for you?

103

Alice: Well, the bad part for me was that after you've been doing it for a while, you change your whole way of thinking. And I became very zombie-ish. While you're high, you're one thing, but when you start coming down, that's another. I just couldn't think. And I'd let things slide. And if you are into creating things and want to get anything together in life, that's not the way to do it. There would be times I'd sit there and literally not be able to think. And I realized we were getting into a complete rut, without having the energy or any way to get out of that rut. And the more you took, the more you got into that rut.

Your personality changes too—you're not on top of it, you're below it. And if you're having a relationship with somebody, it gets very, very hard to maintain. Because you're looking at each other for a way out of the mess you're in, and neither of you can help.

I'd been doing it, say, twice a week for a couple of months until I went up to London for a week or so and didn't have anything. Well, my mind started coming back to me, and I realized I hadn't even known it had been away. I started to think clearly and my thoughts came quickly, and I thought, wow, what a difference! You don't realize the difference until you go without it for a while. It took four or five days before my mind cleared up. That stuff stays with you.

Then of course with people on heroin there's no order to their lives. They can't plan anything or get anything together because they're a complete slave to the way the drug is reacting in them. You can't even go away for four or five days, because you might run out of your supply and that would be a horror. So you are basically a captive to the place where your connection is. Which is really bad when you think of people going away for a few days, and you can't do it. It really got me pissed off. I wanted to go away and see a bit of England, but he would never go. We had a lot of fights about that. But no way, he *couldn't* go.

I began looking like I was dead. You just don't care how you look. Then your arms. I didn't do that much, but the others, they'd get all kinds of things on their arms—abcesses, collapsed veins. Terrible. And if one vein collapsed, they'd just start using another, and if the whole arm was gone, they'd shoot in their ankles. Oh, it's perverted, being a pincushion.

You said you liked the needle.

Alice: Yeah, I dig it. Right. But those people were *really* into needles. They didn't care *what* happened to their arms or anything else. If you want to be a zombie, you go into heroin the way they're into it. It's all a matter of what you want, I guess, and I don't want that.

Their lives are so horrible. They can only exist by ripping off, hustling, borrowing money, scoring, shooting and then worrying about getting the next fix. And that's their life every single day.

The Addict
and the Law

Everyone agrees that drug addiction is a serious problem, but not everyone agrees *why* it is a serious problem. Some put their emphasis on addiction itself, others on addict-related crime, and a smaller number see our national drug policies as the primary cause of the present distressing situation. And though there is wide disagreement on what our national policy on drugs *should* be, no one seriously disagrees on what in fact our policy *is*. It is, and has been since 1914, to treat addiction to, and the use of, narcotic drugs as a law enforcement problem rather than a medical one. In effect, we have decided to be the addict-user's judge rather than his physician.

In this role we label him a criminal, an action which allows us in all good conscience to jail him outright, jail him politely through civil commitment proceedings or, as is being increasingly done, assign him to a methadone program. And whatever we do to him, we justify our action with the belief that narcotics addicts and users are menaces both to themselves and society. So whatever we do, we do for their good and ours.

But no matter how we express our rationalizations, they seem to rest on a strong foundation of moral righteousness. A clear indication of this implicit moral reproof is the constant employment of the phrase "drug abuser," a phrase used to describe anyone who ingests drugs not condoned by the law. It is a description not of fact, but of our attitudes. For there is no distinction in fact between the casual marijuana smoker and the moderate taker of prescription tranquilizers which justifies the one being called a "drug abuser" and the other not. There is only a distinction in law, a law which purportedly embodies national attitudes on drugs.

Of course no one expects a society not to have a set of generally accepted norms, those things which are regarded as acceptable behavior and those which are seen as unacceptable. Every society does have them, and they are usually most powerful in the areas of religion, sexual mores, and life-styles. The question always is how far should a society go in imposing its norms on individual members. And the framers of our Constitution had a healthy fear of society's tendency to dictate the way its members might lead their lives. As a consequence, the Constitution expressly forbade any law which could limit religious freedom. And the Bill of Rights makes clear, or should make clear, that a person's sexual and living preferences are to be of his own choosing. The Ninth Amendment states the matter succinctly: "The enumeration in the Constitution, of certain rights, shall not be construed to deny or disparage others retained by the people." Since the Constitution says nothing about sex, nor does it mention the taking of drugs, illicit or otherwise, any laws designed to circumscribe individual behavior in these areas extend the state's power over the citizens beyond anything contemplated by the writers of the Constitution.

Of course our legislatures *have* passed such laws, making what the majority either doesn't do or doesn't like, illegal. Not satisfied with scorning our neighbors' tastes, we impose criminal sanctions on them. This procedure is known as legislating morality. There are a vast number of such laws, few of which are obeyed and few of which are not being actively challenged and overturned. The Blue Laws which prohibit the sale of many kinds of goods and services on Sunday are now being honored mostly in the breach. The Volstead Act, which initiated the Prohibition Era, was repealed. Abortion is legal in the more progressive states. Laws forbidding the dissemination of birth control devices are being found unconstitutional. The crazy quilt of ordinances prohibiting a number of sexual acts between men and women are, when still on the books, ignored. The laws against homosexuality are under strong challenge. The pressures for legalizing marijuana are increasing. And there is now some serious consideration being given to the legalization of heroin.

Viewing all this, many fundamentalists see us fast becoming a nation of perverts and degenerates, proceeding headlong down the road of moral decay. They preach against the "new liberality" as if all the practices they deplore were new and never before known in the land. But this is not so. All that has really changed is that people are acting more openly. Goods were bought and sold on Sunday in the past. Gangster dynasties were founded on the profits reaped during Prohibition. Butchers grew rich on back-alley abortions. No one who knew about and wanted contraceptive devices went without them. Men and women who wished to vary their sexual acts did so. Men who loved men never stopped loving them in compliance to laws. And those who used opiates and other illicit drugs continued to use them.

Most of this activity took place not because the participants were committed to a lawless life, but because they did not feel they were doing wrong in the way the laws said they were. They were involved in transactions between willing buyers and willing sellers. The "crimes" they were committing and are committing are crimes without victims.

The nation's feelings of moral righteousness respecting its legislating of tastes is nowhere more evident than in its attitudes toward the use of heroin. So long as a claim is made that some new measure will help resolve the problem, we have been willing to countenance it, no matter

110

how inhumane it may be. But close to sixty years of escalating repression has only made the price of heroin prohibitive and consequently increased addict-related crime, generated more heroin addicts, and made the problem worse in every way. The cost of this policy to addicts, users, their families, and victims is great; and the cost to the nation, simply in terms of policing, jailing, and treatment is enormous. And the costs have grown greater with each passing year.

Why, then, has a drug policy which has failed miserably on every level been given such widespread and largely uncritical support? How did we manage to make such a mess of things?

To begin with, the public would never have supported so unsuccessful a policy for so long had it not been convinced that opiate use was harmful to the public welfare. It does believe this to be the case and believes it on the basis of a sixty-year propaganda campaign conducted by the BNDD and its supporters. This campaign has conveyed a wide variety of erroneous ideas about opiates and addiction, five of which appear to have greatly influenced, indeed probably have *formed*, the nation's attitude towards opiate use:

1 *Once an opiate addict, always an opiate addict.*
   —There is evidence that a goodly proportion of heroin users stop using in their thirties and forties. Dr. Charles Winick first proposed the "maturing out" hypothesis in 1962,[1] and studies since that time indicate that perhaps as many as one-third of all addicts cease use sometime in their thirties and forties. Canada's Ledain Commission noted "that there are only a few middle-aged persons who are dependent on opiate narcotics. Most individuals spontaneously lose interest in the drugs before they turn

111

forty-five years of age (barbiturate and alcohol dependents show no such decline in use). Whether this is due to psychological or physiological factors is uncertain."[2] There are no statistical studies, however, that support the Ledain Commission's contention that there are only a "few middle-aged persons" dependent on narcotics. And data from the pre-Harrison era certainly indicates a great many middle-aged opiate addicts in that period.

2 *The use of opiates causes serious physiological damage to the user.*
—No one has found any long-term organic damage caused by opiate use or addiction. The classical study on the physiological effects of prolonged opiate use found that other than those effects atributable to the addict life-style, long-term opiate use was not characterized by either physical deterioration or impairment of physical fitness.[3] Even microscopic examination of body tissues during autopsy fails to show evidence of organic damage. Accepted current medical opinion on the effects of heroin on the body can be summed up as follows: "While there is ample evidence that the aberrant way of life followed by most heroin abusers has both acute and chronic medical consequences . . . there is insufficient scientific basis for maintaining that long-term use of opiates—in and of itself—is related to any major medical condition."[4]

Indeed, heroin is very low on the list of physically damaging drugs. Dr. Samuel Irwin has ranked the common drugs of abuse in the following descending order of dangerousness:[5]

Glue-sniffing
Methamphetamine (speed)
Alcohol

Cigarettes
Barbiturates and hypnotics
Heroin and related narcotics
LSD and other hallucinogens
Marijuana

3 *The use of opiates makes it impossible for a user to work, and thus he cannot contribute to society.*

—This is a complex question, but it can be briefly noted that neither opiate use nor opiate addiction need impair one's ability to work. As one authority has put it, "The number of professionally successful persons who were or are addicted to opiates is an indication that there is no necessary relationship between opiate use and an unproductive life."[6] And Terry and Pellens make it clear that prior to the criminalization of the opiate user, regular productive work was the rule rather than the exception for addicts.[7]

4 *The use of opiates leads to crime, especially crimes against property. Since he is unfit for regular work, the addict must steal to support his habit.*

—It is a wonder this argument is still propounded, but one need only consult one's local newspaper to read the latest restatement of it. The plain and simple truth is that neither heroin use nor heroin addiction leads to crime. What leads the addict-user to crime are laws which make the use of heroin a crime and the resulting exorbitant price of heroin, a price which only a tiny minority of users could possibly raise by legitimate means.

5 *The use of opiates releases or stimulates violent and antisocial behavior.*

—Translated, this is the notion that the user of opiates becomes a drug-crazed dope-fiend with a

113

special taste for rape and mayhem, and a predilection for turning innocent young girls into prostitutes.

One rarely sees this silly notion expressed these days, but in the past the dope-fiend mythology worked wonders for the BNDD and its allies. Nothing served so well to gain and keep support for their law enforcement philosophy. Not the least of its charms was that it was a belief which easily evaded refutation. For it didn't have its genesis in official "scientific" studies, but in sensational newspaper stories and equally sensational popular novels. And if anyone doubts that such sources can be powerful influences, he should look back to the 1950s, when the coverage given Senator Joseph McCarthy led a substantial majority of the American people to believe that the government was inundated with Communist agents.

The development of the dope-fiend mythology probably began in the 1870's when Chinese laborers were brought into the country to work on the construction of the Southern Pacific Railroad. Many brought their opium pipes with them and soon the newspapers were carrying accounts of the Chinese "vice." And soon the nation was alarmed over the connection the press made between opium and "illicit" sex. What had happened was that the newspapers parlayed two established facts—prostitution and opium use—into something a good deal more titillating and salable, the white-slave traffic. Now a good many prostitutes did use opium as a means to impeding the menstrual flow. So a connection existed between opium use and prostitution. And the press had used white-slave stories to build circulation. They then drew a connection between white-slave traffic and opium which their readers apparently accepted as fact. According to these stories, girls were plied with opium and then, their wills destroyed, their bodies ravaged, were forced into prostitution. That this ever happened is extremely doubtful but a good part of the public believed it did.

Then in 1913, *The Insidious Dr. Fu-Manchu,* the first of Sax Rohmer's twenty novels featuring the evil doctor appeared. And like the Mr. Nixon of 1968, the insidious Doctor had a plan. Unlike Mr. Nixon's plan, it was concise and plainly stated: Fu-Manchu intended to enslave the white world with his evil drugs. Whether the chief weapon was to be opium or cocaine is not really clear. Rohmer and Fu-Manchu were somewhat confused about these polar-opposite drugs. Indeed so confused that the reader could not be blamed for taking them as synonyms.

The Fu-Manchu novels, their serializations, and the movies made from them were very popular and made Sax Rohmer a rich man. They also made the public believers in the drug-crazed dope-fiend vicious criminal stereotype. That opiates produce not violent impulses to rape, murder, and general mayhem but quite the opposite—a notable tendency to relax and withdraw was completely overlooked, an oversight partially attributable to the confusion between cocaine and opium. Cocaine does, in a few individuals, with prolonged and large dosages, produce violent and unpredictable behavior. As does alcohol. The opiates, as sedative analgesics, do not. "As the great Joseph Lister observed, opium soothes while alcohol maddens. In the turn of the century America, while their fellows were being incapacitated in ever larger numbers by drink, drug users, able to maintain their supplies without difficulty and at modest expense, generally pursued normal callings and posed no problems for society."[8]

The sensationalistic and money-making use of the dope-fiend myth certainly affected the public's attitude toward drug users, but it was not until passage of the

Harrison Narcotics Act in 1914 that the addict-user himself was seriously threatened. Not by the Harrison Act itself—for though it soon enough made it impossible for opiate users to get their supplies "without difficulty and at modest expense," neither the intention nor the language of the bill had any such outcome in mind—but by the use made of the act by certain bureaucrats.

What happened is a classic example of an uninformed Congress and an uninformed public being manipulated by a bureaucracy for its own ends. Just as the senators who voted for the Gulf of Tonkin Resolution did not foresee or intend that President Johnson would use it to justify a full-scale war, neither did the framers and passers of Harrison intend that it be used to make criminals of opiate users and of the doctors who wrote their prescriptions. The act was passed as a revenue and record-keeping measure and nothing more. It came into being chiefly because the American delegation to the first International Opium Convention at The Hague in 1912 had pushed strongly for all governments concerned to establish internal controls over narcotics. Rather embarrassingly, America itself had no such controls, and the Harrison Act was drafted to relieve this embarrassment and to serve as a model for other nations.[9] Consistent with these intentions, the Harrison Act required that "special forms be used when drugs were transferred and ... that persons and firms handling drugs register and pay fees," requirements certainly appropriate to making the distribution of drugs a matter of record.[10] As Alfred Lindesmith and others have pointed out, "There is no indication of a legislative intention to deny addicts drugs or to interfere in any way with medical practice in this area."[11] The act itself plainly stated that:

Nothing contained in this section shall apply: (a) to the dispensing or distribution of any of the aforesaid drugs to a patient by a physician, dentist, or veterinary surgeon registered under this Act in the course of his professional practice only.[12]

And though on the face of it the Harrison Act did little more than require that persons and firms importing and distributing drugs register and pay a nominal tax on their goods, it further required that all narcotic drugs be obtained from physicians registered under the act. Thus all those who were previously getting their narcotics from pharmacies and mail-order houses now needed doctors' prescriptions. This apparently sensible and innocuous requirement was instrumental in developing the narcotic black market, for a small percentage of the addict population was poor and neither knew how nor could afford to consult a physician. But of course they still needed their narcotics, and where there is a need, there is always someone who will supply it for the proper consideration. In this care the supplier was the underworld.

The Harrison Act contained other language which was to prove troublesome. For though in one section it clearly stated its intention of not interfering with medical practices, other sections qualified this clear statement, leaving it open to interpretation. For example, physicians could dispense drugs only for "legitimate medical purposes," and the drugs had to be "prescribed in good faith."[13] Unfortunately, nothing in the act defined these these phrases, and subsequent Treasury Department interpretations and court decisions turned the Harrison Act into something quite different from what had been intended by the Congress. Precisely how this happened and its consequences, are best described in Alfred Lindesmith's 1956 essay, "Federal Law and Drug Addiction," and what follows respecting Harrison is largely based on Professor Lindesmith's work.

117

The Harrison Act said nothing about the legal status of the addict; it neither made addiction illegal not forbade doctors from prescribing drugs to addicts. The subsequent criminalization of the addict came through the instrumentalities of the courts and the law enforcement officers charged with implementing the act.

The first step in this process was the 1915 Supreme Court decision in U.S. v. Jim Fuey Moy,[14] which ruled that possession of smuggled drugs by an addict was a violation of the act. The defense had argued that the section of the act relied upon for this ruling referred only to those persons, physicians and other distributors of drugs, required to register under the act. The defense had a sound argument. To make possession of illegal drugs a crime for persons not even mentioned in the act—in this case, addicts—created a whole class of criminals by judicial fiat. Put another way, it was a clear case of *ad hoc* lawmaking.

Then in 1919 in Webb v. U.S.,[15] the Court ruled that any prescription of drugs for an addict not given in the course of an attempted cure of his addiction but given only to provide the user with enough morphine to keep him comfortable, was not a prescription within the meaning of the law and thus not included within the exemptions provided for in the doctor-patient relationship. In reaching this decision the Court gave no indication that it had consulted medical opinion. A contrary interpretation of the law, it said, "would be so plain a perversion of meaning that no discussion is required." (It was the Justices who were perverse. They were judges, not doctors, yet they implicitly claimed to have full knowledge of "legitimate medical purposes" in a field as complex as drug addiction.)

A year later[16] the Court decided that a doctor could

not legitimately prescribe drugs "to cater to the appetite or satisfy the craving of one addicted to the use of drugs." And in 1922 in U.S. v. Behrman,[17] the Court went a step further in supporting the notion that there was no legitimate way in which a doctor could prescribe drugs for an addict. It ruled that such prescriptions were illegal, no matter what purpose the doctor had in mind. By this decision doctors were deprived of the defense that they had acted in good faith, since "Dr. Behrman was convicted despite the fact that the prosecution stipulated that he had prescribed drugs in order to treat and cure addicts."[18]

The addict, who had not been mentioned in the Harrison Act, now had a clear position under the law: he was denied all access to legal drugs. The inhumanity and injustice exhibited here is truly reprehensible. People who had become addicted to opiates during a time when opiate use was as legal as eating ice cream, were now in effect told they would have to grin and bear it.

These prosecutions and the interpretations of the Harrison Act which informed them were, as we have already noted, contrary to the intention of the act. They came about because a small band of Treasury officials—since it was a revenue act, the Treasury Department was charged with enforcing it—supported by a handful of doctors, had decided that addiction was not a disease, "but a willful indulgence meriting punishment rather than medical treatment."[19]

Lester D. Volk, a physician and a New York Congressman, charged in a 1922 speech from the House floor that

There has developed a tendency in carrying out the objects of the Harrison Law to substitute for the provisions of the act arbitrary administrative opinions expressed in rules and regulations which amount to practically a repeal and nullification of the law itself.

These rules and regulations have been promulgated by those in charge of the administration of the Harrison Law upon the representation and statements coming as the official pronouncements of the New York City Board of Health, presented by a particular small group or clique ... Reliable records, reports, scientific information, and experience have been swept aside by these men and in their place has been set up a campaign of publicity intended in the end to benefit this small coterie who seek to control the avenues of narcotic treatment throughout the country.

The agitation emanating from New York City from these men [Volk had named them earlier] and the Department of Health is spreading over the entire country and knowingly or unknowingly has evaded and ignored sound medical findings. As a substitute for open discussion of known medical facts there has been set up a propaganda for the incarceration of all drug users ... An undeniable effort is now being made whereby physicians are to be denied any discretion and power in the prescribing of narcotic drugs and to force all those addicted to the use of drugs into hospitals exploiting questionable "cures."[20]

As Lindesmith has pointed out, the legal situation respecting doctors and addicts was at least relatively clear by 1922. Repressive, but relatively clear. The court decisions and the rules handed down by the Treasury Department were evidence enough that private doctors could not treat addicts in "any way acceptable to law enforcement officials."[21] Only in the case of "aged and infirm addicts in whom withdrawal might cause death and in the case of persons afflicted with such diseases as incurable cancer" was the dispensation of narcotic drugs legal.[22]

Given such a state of affairs, it was hardly surprising that few doctors were willing to jeopardize their careers by treating addicts. Those who did were threatened with prosecution. The underground traffic in narcotics blossomed gorgeously.

The legal situation got somewhat muddled in 1925 with the Linder case.

> Unlike the doctors in the earlier cases, Dr. Linder, a Seattle practitioner, provided only four tablets of drugs for one addict. The addict, a woman, came to his office in a state of partial withdrawal and he provided her with drugs to be used at her discretion. She was an informer who reported the incident to the police and Dr. Linder was prosecuted for criminal violation of the law. Judging from the previous court decisions and from the Treasury Department regulations in force at the time, Linder should have been convicted, and he was. The lower court could hardly have reached any other decision, for Dr. Linder had obviously given drugs to this user to relieve withdrawal distress and to maintain customary usage and there was no thought of cure.[23]

After prolonged litigation, the Linder decision was reversed by the Supreme Court. The litigation reportedly cost Dr. Linder $30,000. He had also suffered a two-year loss of his medical license. The Court commented on the cases mentioned above, putting particular stress on the fact that all of them had involved the dispensing of large amounts of drugs and that subsequent decisions had to be considered in the light of this. Commenting on the Harrison Act itself, the Court said:

> It says nothing of "addicts" and does not undertake to prescribe methods for their medical treatment. They are diseased and proper subjects for such treatment, and we cannot possibly conclude that a physician acted improperly or unwisely or for other than medical purposes solely because he has dispensed to one of them, in the ordinary course and in good faith, four small tablets of morphine or cocaine for relief of conditions incident to addiction. What constitutes bona fide medical practice must be determined upon consideration of evidence and attending circumstances.[24]

121

This is a long way from Behrman, three years before, when the Court in effect ruled that there was no legitimate way for a private doctor to prescribe drugs to an addict.

Commenting on the Webb case, the Court said that the rule formulated in it

> must not be construed as forbidding every prescription of drugs, irrespective of quantity, when designed temporarily to alleviate an addict's pains, although it may have been issued in good faith and without design to defeat the revenues.[25]

The Court commented in the same vein on Behrman and warned that

> The opinion cannot be accepted as authority for holding that a physician who acts bona fide and according to fair medical standards may never give an addict moderate amounts of drugs for self-administration in order to relieve conditions incident to addiction. Enforcement of the tax demands no such drastic rule, and if the Act had such scope it would certainly encounter grave constitutional difficulties.[26]

In short, the Supreme Court made it plain in the Linder case that it regarded addiction as a disease and made it a rule that it was not necessarily a violation of the law for a physician to give an addict moderate amounts of drugs to relieve withdrawal symptoms if the physician acted in good faith and according to fair medical standards.

And in 1936 in U.S. v. Anthony, Federal Judge Yankwich summed up the consequences of the Linder opinion in the following way:

> I am satisfied therefore, that the Linder case, and the cases which interpret it, lay down the rule definitely that the statute does not say what drugs a physician may prescribe an addict. Nor does it say the quantity which a physician may or may not prescribe. Nor does it regulate the frequency of prescription. Any attempt to so interpret the

statute, by an administrative interpretation, whether that administrative interpretation be oral, in writing, or by an officer or by a regulation of the department, would be not only contrary to the law, but would also make the law unconstitutional as being clearly a regulation of the practice of medicine.[27]

According to this view, the Treasury Department's implementation of Harrison was based on unconstitutional interpretations, and the present law enforcement policy, which differs very little from the old in essentials, is in clear violation of federal law. But no doctor reading this should be so foolish as to rely upon the law of the land and set about prescribing narcotics if in his judgment an addict requires them. For neither Linder nor subsequent cases had any effect on enforcement policies. Federal law enforcement officials simply chose to ignore the rules given in the Linder opinion. They continued prosecuting doctors as if Linder and the rules did not exist. Both before and after the Linder case, the Narcotics Division of the Treasury Department strongly enforced its view that addiction was not a disease and that maintaining addicts on opiates was not acceptable practice. Between the years 1914 and 1938 some 25,000 doctors were arraigned for supplying narcotics to addicts, and some 3,000 of them went to jail.[28]

These Draconian measures, though extralegal, were not altogether arbitrary. They were undertaken on the mistaken belief that once an addict was deprived of his drug and had gone through withdrawal, his problems were over. And the authorities were not shy in expressing this view. The preface to the Prohibition Bureau's Regulations contains the following remarkable statement: "It is well established that the ordinary case of addiction will yield to proper treatment, and that addicts will remain permanently cured when drug addiction is stopped and they are otherwise physically restored to health and strengthened in will power."[29] Except for the fact that, as the context makes plain, the writer means "drug use" rather than "drug addiction," this is a pretty fair statement of the Treasury Department's beliefs regarding opiate addiction. It is also a pretty fair example of wildly overstating a case. Far from this view being well-established, the vast majority of medical practitioners of the era who were acquainted with opiate addiction held a contrary view.[30] As they do now.

If the Treasury Department was given to establishing nonsense as official creed, it nevertheless had not at that date developed the moral wrath which its few supporters in the medical community were able to summon up against their fellow doctors. Rufus King quotes a member of the AMA's Committee on Narcotic Drugs, purportedly speaking officially for the Association in 1921: "The shallow pretense that drug addiction is a disease which the specialist must be allowed to treat, which pretended treatment consists in supplying its victims with the drug which has caused their physical and moral debauchery . . . has been asserted and urged in volumes of literature by the self-styled specialists."[31] Spiro Agnew couldn't have said it better.

Given such beliefs respecting addiction, it was easy for law enforcement officials to view doctors who prescribed narcotics to addicts as nothing more than drug pushers, and prosecute them accordingly—which they did, despite Linder and other court decisions to the contrary. And given such policies, few reputable doctors were or are willing to risk their careers by practicing in accordance with their medical beliefs. Similarly, few lower federal court judges were willing to follow the precedents of the

Linder case, for this would have mean "upsetting an established enforcement policy vigorously supported by police propaganda."[32] What the lower courts *did* do was to interpret Linder as merely *supplementing* rather than replacing the older rules. In practice this resulted in the rules from the Webb case and the rules from the Linder case—rules which were mutually incompatible—being applied simultaneously in a situation where a doctor treated an addict with narcotics. This meant that in theory no such doctor could be sure whether he would be convicted under the first or acquitted under the second[33] —in theory, because in practice Linder was almost never used. A better example of bad law can hardly be imagined.

There has been considerable federal and state legislation on the narcotics question since the Harrison Act, but the basic patterns of our law enforcement policy have never been changed. Apart from provisions which make it easier to procure convictions and provisions which limit the discretion of judges in sentencing, the principal change had been the incorporation of harsher penalties. The Boggs Bill of 1951, the Narcotic Drug Control Act of 1956, and the Comprehensive Drug Abuse Prevention & Control Act of 1970, the chief federal additions, all run along these lines. What we have, and have had since 1914, to determine the legitimate needs and treatment of addicts is not a medical policy but a law enforcement policy—policemen who tell doctors what they can and can't do for a patient.

The law-enforcing machine did not roll on unopposed. Sane men in the medical and legal communities fought it manfully. They were either ignored, harassed, or actively threatened. Some examples:

Dr. Charles Terry, Health Officer of Jacksonville, Florida, a man with long experience in treating addicts and administering clinics, and later coauthor of the classic work, *The Opium Problem,* wrote the following in 1920:

> Narcotic drug addiction-disease will never be solved by forcible measures alone. There is a place and a great need for such measures and they should be limited to this field alone, namely to the control of traffickers, exploiters, charlatans and quacks.
>
> Yet even here police measures to be successful must go hand in hand with intelligent medical services. If anyone doubts this let him try to extinguish the underground traffic in narcotic drugs by police measures alone. Experience has shown this to be impossible during the four years' enforcement of various restrictive legislative and administrative experiments.[34]

Dr. Terry's sound advice was ignored, and some fifty-two years after he wrote, we have an illicit narcotics traffic too large and too widespread to be estimated accurately. And far from being extinguished, the drug traffic grows larger each year.

Congressman Lester D. Volk, M.D., in the 1922 speech quoted before, gave a detailed analysis of what had happened in New York under the prevailing enforcement policy. At one point he said,

> . . . apparently it takes but a twist of the wrist of the Revenue Department at the bidding of ignorant and egotistic, self-centered, and perhaps criminally inclined professional men and administrators to put in force in these United States a set of regulations, drastic in their inception, unethical in their administration, and calamitous in their effect.[35]

These are strong charges, but the House never investigated them.

Dr. Ernest S. Bishop, Consulting Physician to the New York State Prison Commission and one of the nation's leading authorities on addiction, was a strong and persistent critic of the manner in which the Harrison Act had been interpreted and implemented. "For this opposition," said Congressman Volk,

> Dr. Bishop was indicted . . . [for alleged violations of the Harrison Act] . . . His persecution is a medical and political scandal and an obstruction to the solution of the drug problem.[36]

Dr. Bishop was never brought to trial. The indictment was held over his head for some years and then withdrawn by another prosecutor who denounced it as "outrageous."[37] But it had served its purpose. If a man of Dr. Bishop's stature could be so harassed for speaking his views, who was safe?

In the Interim Report of the Joint Committee of the American Bar Association and the American Medical Association on Narcotic Drugs (1958), the Committee said— and supported its charge with documentation—that the policy of treating addiction as a crime had failed and that it was about time we treated it for what it was, a disease. The Joint Committee, which consisted of six distinguished members of the two associations, presented the Interim Report to Harry Anslinger for comments and criticism. Mr. Anslinger then wrote a letter to Judge Morris Ploscowe, former Chief Magistrate of New York City and one of the chief authors of the report, strongly condemning it: "I find it incredible that so many glaring inaccuracies, apparent ambiguities, important omissions, and even false statements could be found in one report on the narcotic problem."[38] After such a statement, one might have expected that Mr. Anslinger had any number of specific criticisms to make. But when asked by the Joint Committee to provide a bill of particulars, Mr. Anslinger refused and instead appointed an Advisory Committee to the Federal Bureau of Narcotics and charged it with the task of replying to the Interim Report. The members of this committee were mainly policemen, prosecuting attorneys, and others who agreed with the Bureau's handling of the narcotics problem. They published a very crude and intemperate criticism of the Interim Report, the most interesting part of which was its physical appearance. It had "a title, format, and color which made it hard to distinguish from the Interim Report itself."[39] Professor Benjamin DeMott characterized this duplicity and the Bureau's report as perhaps "the crudest publication yet produced by a government agency."[40]

And this shady maneuver was not the end of the Bureau's attacks on the Joint Committee. The Interim and Final Reports of the Committee were published in 1961 by the Indiana University Press in a book entitled *Drug Addiction: Crime or Disease?* Not only did the Federal Bureau of Narcotics send agents to harass officials of Indiana University, the Indiana University Press, and the Russell Sage Foundation, which financially underwrote the book, but Federal Judge Edward J. Dimock, one of the six members of the Joint Committee, was attacked by Mr. Anslinger, testifying before a House subcommittee, as a man so notoriously soft on narcotics traffickers that "many of these defendants . . . try to maneuver their cases so they come before [him], and of course they naturally waive a jury trial and are tried by the judge himself."[41]

Mr. Anslinger's 1962 slander of Judge Dimock was duly circulated by the press. And slander it was, based as far as any records show solely on the fact that Judge Dimock had reduced the bail of three men charged with conspiracy in an international narcotics case from $250,000 to $50,000 each—an action he took in obedience to the Eighth Amendment, which specifies that excessive bail shall not be required of persons not charged with capital crimes.

Disagreement, then, with the nation's drug policies has historically been subject to massive retaliation rather than the consideration honest criticism merits. Since Harry Anslinger's retirement as head of the Federal Bureau of Narcotics, however, the vituperative attacks on the motives and characters of individual critics have not been so common. Now officials counter proposals contrary to their policies by either claiming that they have been tried before and have failed—the tack taken, for example, against those who have proposed heroin maintenance clinics, and a dubious tack at that, as we shall see in Chapter VI—or by claiming that more research is needed to "establish the facts," the argument they usually make when proposals are made to lessen or abolish the marijuana penalties.

As brutal and misconceived as our drug policies have been, there might be some argument for them had they proved effective. But our drug policies have patently failed us. No American capable of reading, listening to a radio, or watching television, and certainly no American living in one of our major cities, has any doubt about their ineffectiveness. Unfortunately, as we who have lived through countless statements about lights at the end of the tunnel know, our governments seem to learn little from past errors. And once the errors have been codified into policy, they take on an aura of holy writ. The Harrison Act was misused to make addiction illegal, thus generating an extensive black market in drugs. This creation of the law enforcers was then used by them to justify further excesses in repression and of course to justify their failure to eliminate it:

There's a demand in the United States for heroin that's unbelievable. In order to stop it, you'd have to put every

129

law enforcement agency you have in the United States just to work on narcotics alone. Plus the U.S. Army. And I still don't think you'd stop it.[42]

The great villain for narcotics officers and their supporters has always been their own child, the drug dealer. To them, nothing is worse than a drug dealer—rapists and murderers notwithstanding. Mr. Nixon recently called drug trafficking "the most reprehensible of all crimes . . . worse than a crime like murder." [43] Indeed, so great has been their loathing of the dealers and so great the official zeal for eliminating them, that at one point Harry Anslinger made the incredible suggestion that jailing users would be a very effective way of attacking their dealers:

> From the practical standpoint it is fundamental that a business, legal or illegal, would be bound to fail if deprived of customers, and the peddler of narcotic drugs is no exception. If the peddler were deprived of a market for his illegal wares, he would cease to exist. As long as the addict is at liberty to come and go, the peddler has a steady customer.[44]

It would be equally sensible to eliminate the common cold by encasing every citizen in a plastic cocoon. But in all fairness it should be noted that Mr. Anslinger's suggestion was perhaps motivated by the fact that while addicts are easy to apprehend, dealers of any magnitude are very hard to catch. Then too it was made when Anslinger was claiming there were 60,000 heroin addicts in the country, and though no one familiar with his activities would doubt his readiness to add them to our prison population, it is doubtful he would try to justify the expense of incarcerating the 560,000 addicts now estimated by federal officials.

The rationale informing our long-held policy of using law enforcement techniques as the chief weapons for combating heroin addiction has always been beautifully simple: if no heroin is available, there will be no heroin addicts. Unarguably, this is true. Of course addicts would then turn to any number of other opiates, synthetic and otherwise, but the *heroin* problem would be licked.

That it hasn't been is really not due to the laxity of the drug police, even though widespread corruption has reduced their efficiency. They have striven mightily and in greatly increased numbers over the past few years to gain the final victory. The fault lies with their mission; it is an impossible one. On the federal level it has been, until very recently, the elimination of major traffickers, and while sensational news stories claiming the breakup of major international dope rings and the consequent disruption of the domestic heroin scene appear frequently, the true effect of these operations has been negligible. Of course some officials connected with these operations *do* make modest claims of success. Commenting on the great increase in the number of sizable heroin seizures made during 1971, as compared to previous years, Eugene T. Rossides, Assistant Secretary of the Treasury, said that ". . . these huge seizures of heroin, in addition to causing appreciable financial losses to the traffickers . . . have had *some* effect on supply." [45] (italics added) But New York Police Department officials, responding to this statement, discounted the claim that the supply had been affected: "the price of heroin has remained steady in recent months and there has been no panic." [46] Similarly, Whitney North Seymour Jr., U.S. Attorney for the Southern District of New York, said that "the impact has not been significant . . ." [47] And New York junkies with whom I have talked agree with the local police that price and availability have remained steady: "You take the same bread to the same guy and get the same shit."

131

The notion that heroin can be stopped from entering the country is absurd. Approximately 250 million people enter the country every year; some sixty-five million motor vehicles, 306,000 planes, and 157,000 ships entered in 1970.[48] And even if it was possible to screen adequately this vast entry—and it is not—there remains the thousands of miles of borderland shared with Canada and Mexico, plus thousands of miles of coastline to patrol, most of which afford easy entry to the smuggler. So long as our national drug policy declares the addict a criminal and leaves him only illicit sources to meet his needs, the only way of seriously impeding the highly profitable flow of heroin is by shutting down the borders and sealing the coastline. That is, by implementing a full-scale police-state. Russia has but a very small heroin problem, and we could reduce ours substantially by employing like methods.

This can't be done without scrapping the Constitution, however, and so the Feds, having failed to stop the flow of heroin, save their pride and budgets by arguing that their costly efforts have a deterrent effect. That is, seizures make the distributors more cautious, and being more cautious they don't move their heroin so quickly.[49] In fact it is probable that large seizures affect the heroin market in a quite different way. Breaking up major operations leaves room for many smaller operators to move in and compete with the established firms. The more big firms eliminated, the more room for small independents. And a competitive industry

> will always provide more goods at lower prices than will a monopoly. Market expansion would occur if lower prices increase the demand for heroin, and, in fact, this may be occurring. Two very large seizures by the BNDD in May and June of 1970 reportedly had no effect on price. No panics occurred following the seizures, as one would expect, and

the short-term trend over the year was one of declining prices.[50]

It may now be evident to the reader that law enforcement has not been an adequate tool for working on the heroin problem. Unfortunately this fact has not appeared evident to our government: "Prodded by the growing number of addicts and of addict-related crime, both Federal and local authorities have redoubled their efforts to get at the suppliers of heroin . . ."[51] And through 1971, the major federal efforts were still directed at the big international traffickers. But apparently the government has realized that its efforts and our money have brought us all pitifully small returns. The focus has been changed. Instead of concentrating on big dealers, the Feds are now putting their money on the lower-level dealers. A new Office of Drug Enforcement in the Justice Department, under Myles J. Ambrose, has been set up to do precisely that. "Our task," Mr. Ambrose told a news conference on February 18, 1972, "is to get as many pushers as possible off the street, to develop an intelligence network that will make it increasingly difficult for others to operate and to stimulate state and local police and prosecutors to attack the problem."[52] Mr. Ambrose went on to say that the new offensive against the "little fellow" was not an end in itself, but was intended to lead to the big dealers.

Mr. Ambrose has the full support of his Commander-in-Chief, President Nixon, who officially opened the new campaign by declaring "total war against Public Enemy Number One." There is, he continued, "no penalty that is too great for the traffickers in narcotics." And while education and treatment were important,

> a strong, tough prosecution is an absolutely indispensable part of this program. I can think of nothing on the domestic front more important.[53]

133

To begin with, the street-level dealer has hardly been neglected as claimed by the Administration. Apart from the addict himself, the street dealer has always been the prime target of local narc activity—much to the disgust of many working narcs with whom I have spoken. Their disgust stems not from any liking they have of the dealers, but from the fact that arresting the dealers brings no appreciable results other than relieving neighborhood pressures "to do something." As one narcotics officer said, "if he [the street dealer] gets busted, there's six guys waiting to take his job." [54] And the arrest of a street dealer almost never leads to the apprehension of a middle-level dealer, let alone a major trafficker. The street dealer doesn't *know* a middle-level man; all he knows is the man who supplies him. This supplier is a lower-level operator too, and all *he* knows is the man who supplies *him,* the man who buys in one-kilo lots. And all the one-kilo man knows is the ten-kilo man, and so on up the ladder. There are layers and layers of protection between any big dealer and the street. And layers and layers of muscle. If the street-level dealer is a junkie, he may inform on his supplier, but very few dealers above the street level ever get fingered by a street man. For two reasons. First, the street dealer rarely knows anyone beyond his supplier; and second, informing on people above you in the chain usually carries unpleasant consequences. You get killed. And few street dealers, even junkie street dealers who can be influenced by a police offer of drugs to forestall withdrawal pains, are so foolish as to trade immediate relief for future final relief.

So after nearly sixty years of treating drug addiction as a law enforcement problem rather than a medical problem, and after nearly sixty years of overwhelming evidence that this policy has failed, the total war on what President Nixon calls Public Enemy Number One is to rely mainly on more and stricter law enforcement. If any further evidence need be given to show how ineffective law enforcement is in treating a disease, one need only look at New York City, where most authorities estimate that half the addict-users in the country live. For the period 1968 through 1970, the New York Police Department reported slightly over 51,000 arrests on felony narcotics charges: 9,000 in 1968, 20,000 in 1969 and 26,000 in 1970. [55] Meanwhile, the list of addict-users on the city's Narcotics Register increased by some 103,000 during the same period: 12,000 new names in 1968, 36,604 new names in 1969 and 55,000 new names in 1970.[56]

Law enforcement advocates argue that what has been wrong has not been their policy, but the methods used by the police. Most arrests, they say, were "bad" arrests. (Bad arrests are arrests for which convictions can't be obtained.) In 1969, for example, only 6,000 indictments were returned on the 20,000 arrests, and of these, 5,579 ended in either dismissals or acquittals, and only 421 ended in convictions. [57] So instead of facing the obvious, that their policy was wrongheaded, the state appointed a special assistant district attorney for New York City with city-wide jurisdiction over all narcotics cases, and with specific instructions to make fewer but stronger cases against narcotics law violators. The new setup is expected to handle about 6,000 cases per year. [58] But even if this results in a higher conviction rate, and it probably will, there is no reason to believe it will much affect the heroin traffic. The convictions will still chiefly come against addicts and a handful of street dealers, and, as I have pointed out, this does not affect the flow of heroin from the middle-level dealers to the streets. At best, heroin prices might go up under the increased pressure, but all this will mean is that the cost of addict-related crime will go up too.

And this addict-related crime is not confined to addict-users. For our law enforcement policy has not only created a whole class of persons who *must* commit crimes to feed their addiction, and created a business whose profits make the rum-running of the Prohibition Era appear bush-league by comparison, but these profits have corrupted our police. The corruption began early and has kept pace with the increase in traffic and use. What follows is a small sampler of police corruption, culled from but a single source, the New York *Times:*

—. . .a special employee in the Internal Revenue Bureau was arrested yesterday by Special Agents Grunewald and Scully of the Department of Justice . . . on a charge of having accepted a bribe . . . from Julius Densser, whom he had arrested on a charge of dealing in habit-forming drugs. [October 30, 1917]

—A former Deputy Collector of Internal Revenue was held on $6,000 bail yesterday by Federal Judge Learned Hand on two indictments charging extortion of five ounces of cocaine from a druggist and in connection with a bribe relating to the concealment of records in a criminal proceeding. [June 29, 1920]

—A Federal grand jury indicted two patrolmen yesterday on charges of conspiracy to 'conceal and sell heroin.' The patrolmen were accused of 'shaking down' narcotics peddlers, then giving the seized drugs to an intermediary to sell to addicts. [June 29, 1950]

—Two correction officers at the city penitentiary on Rikers Island . . . were arrested June 30 for allegedly delivering $100 from a narcotics peddler to an inmate . . . [July 8, 1953]

—Three narcotics squad detectives . . . were arrested yesterday on charges of attempting to extort $1,500 from an electronics equipment salesman. They were accused of threatening to arrest Shimon Tamari on a narcotics charge unless they were paid off. [June 22, 1958]

—Three city detectives, two investigators from the Nassau County District Attorney's office and a Federal narcotics agent were arrested yesterday on charges of having sold narcotics to peddlers in New York City and Long Island. [December 13, 1967]

—Three police detectives arrested Tuesday evening on charges of selling narcotics were members of the Police Department's smallest, most sophisticated and least known organization . . . the 30-man Special Investigating Unit of the Narcotics Bureau . . . In an interview yesterday Chief Gardner said that profits from gambling and narcotics generated most of the corruption confronting his division. [December 14, 1967]

—The two Nassau County narcotics investigators who were arrested yesterday with three New York City detectives and a Federal agent on narcotics charges made up the entire Narcotics Bureau of the Nassau District Attorney's office . . . .

Nassau District Attorney William Cahn said: "We know the enormous profits involved in narcotics . . . offered more of an incentive to the defendants than other areas of crime." [December 14, 1967]

—Thirty-two agents who at one time worked in the New York office of the Federal Bureau of Narcotics have resigned since the start of an investigation . . . that has indicated "significant corruption," Attorney General Ramsey Clark said today. [There were eighty agents in the office at the time.]

Mr. Clark predicted that prosecutions and additional resignations would result from the investigation.

So far, he said, five of the 32 former agents have been indicted on charges involving the sale of narcotics. [December 14, 1968]

—. . . last month three detectives were charged with extorting $1,200 in cash, 105 "decks" of heroin and a variety of personal possessions from five New Yorkers. But there is evidence [of] a more regular kind of corruption ... One policeman, with six years of experience in the narcotics division and its elite special investigating unit, said one of his fellow detectives arranged payoffs to policemen from the largest heroin dealer.

These payoffs, he said, ranged from $5,000 for changing testimony just enough so a drug-seller would not be convicted to $50,000 for the sale of a "wire"—the recorded conversation made by a police wiretap or bug.

In at least one case he knew, several of his colleagues collected a great deal of damaging evidence about a major heroin dealer, let the ... payoff arranger know they had the evidence and then waited for a bid from the criminals. The bid came and the money was collected, he said.

... In addition to the graft potential in the narcotics traffic itself, corrupt policemen are in a position to exert considerable pressure on the owners of bars and restaurants. This is because a narcotics arrest in such an establishment means the owner can lose his liquor license. A detective ... said he heard a top commander in the narcotics division chastising another official for not demanding and receiving regular payoffs from the bars in his jurisdiction. [April 25, 1970]

—The chief counsel of the State Commission of Investigation said yesterday that police corruption was one reason the New York Police Department's war against heroin was "a failure, a monumental waste of manpower and money."

... "unfortunately, our investigation has discovered shocking examples of police corruption." These included ... "extortion, bribery, giving contradictory evidence in court to effect the release of narcotics-suspects, improper association with people involved in drugs and the direct involvement of police officers in the sale of narcotics." [April 6, 1971]

The traditional official police response to cases of the kind just listed has always been that "every barrel has a few rotten apples" and that you can't indict a whole police force just because it harbors a "few rogue cops." And traditionally the public has gone along with this view. It is, after all, not easy for the average citizen to accept the fact that the men his taxes pay to enfore the law are very often criminals themselves. But in 1971 the Knapp Commission hearings on police corruption in New York City thoroughly exploded the few-rotten-apples-in-a-barrel defense. The testimony before it clearly showed that police corruption was not only widespread and carefully organized, but known to virtually every officer in the department. On December 27, 1971, Sergeant David Durk, one of the officers whose stories in the New York *Times* gave birth to the Knapp Commission, accurately summed up the situation in these words:

> . . . The most important fact to understand is that I had and have no special knowledge of police corruption. We knew nothing . . . that wasn't known to every man and office in [the police] divisions. We knew nothing about the police traffic in narcotics that wasn't known and testified to here by Paul Curran of the State Investigations Commission. We knew these things because we were involved in law enforcement in New York City, and anyone else who says he didn't know had to be blind, either by choice or by incompetence.

The costs of our law enforcement policy on narcotics and dangerous drugs have been immense. What has been paid in personal suffering, restrictions on every citizen's liberty, and in plain dollars is hard to calculate. But these costs have been well described, in general terms, by Professor Herbert Packer in his book *The Limits of Criminal Sanction:*[59]

> (1) Several hundred thousand people, the overwhelming majority of whom have been primarily users rather than traffickers, have been subjected to severe criminal punishment.

139

(2) An immensely profitable illegal traffic in narcotic and other forbidden drugs has developed.

(3) This illegal traffic has contributed significantly to the growth and prosperity of organized criminal groups.

(4) A substantial number of all acquisitive crimes— burglarly, robbery, auto theft, other forms of larceny—have been committed by drug users to get the wherewithal to pay the artificially high prices charged for drugs on the illegal market.

(5) Billions of dollars and a significant proportion of total law enforcement resources have been expended in all stages of the criminal process.

(6) A disturbingly large number of undesirable police practices—unconstitutional searches and seizures, entrapment, electronic surveillance—have become habitual because of the great difficulty that attends the detection of narcotics offenses.

(7) The burden of enforcement has fallen primarily on the urban poor . . .

(8) Research on the causes, effects, and cures of drug use has been stultified.

(9) The medical profession has been intimidated into neglecting its accustomed role of relieving this form of human misery.

(10) A large and well-entrenched enforcement bureaucracy has developed a vested interest in the status quo, and has effectively thwarted all but the most marginal reforms.

(11) Legislative invocations of the criminal sanction have automatically and unthinkingly been extended from narcotics to marijuana to the flood of new mind-altering drugs that have appeared in recent years, thereby compounding the pre-existing problem.

And it is about time these heavy burdens were weighed against the supposed benefits of this policy. But we will get neither an intelligent nor objective weighing until someone other than policemen control our national drug policy. As Lawrence Kolb, a former Assistant Surgeon General, has written:

> There is no cure except education for the feeling that tolerates and even applauds the results of our present extreme laws and questionable enforcement practices. The first step in the educational process is to eliminate from the minds of the legislators the idea that the people who arrest or prosecute drug addicts have superior knowledge of drug addiction.[60]

In conclusion, it seems clear that as a nation we have long had a tendency to assume that if we did not like something we need merely prohibit it, enforce the prohibition, and that would be the end of the matter. We did not like people getting drunk, so we tried to prohibit them from drinking alcohol. We did not like Vietnam being organized by nationalists and Communists, so we tried to prohibit them from doing it. We did not like people using narcotics, so we tried to prohibit them from using narcotics. But we had to repeal Prohibition because too many people still wanted to drink. The Viet Cong and the North Vietnamese are apparently going to organize Vietnam despite our prohibitions. And more people than ever are using heroin. Perhaps we can learn from history.

The
British Experience

Our law enforcement policy on drugs is clearly a failure, yet our government repeatedly asserts there is no viable alternative to it. The drug problem gets worse every day, and to alleviate it the government escalates a failed policy. What has not worked in the past or present is put forward as the answer to the future. Existing alternatives are said either to not exist or, when this patently absurd ploy is challenged by contrary facts, it is then claimed that these alternatives have been tried in the past and found wanting. This is the game the BNDD and like-minded "experts" play when the British medical approach to addiction is cited as a possible alternative to our law enforcement policy. They either stubbornly maintain that what they term the "so-called British system" is little different from ours[1] or, when this affront to common sense falls of its own silliness, point to the short-lived American clinics of the 1920s as proof that a medical approach to the heroin problem can't possibly work.[2]

The manner in which the Harrison Act was implemented eventually made it impossible for an addict to procure narcotics legally, but for a short period between 1919 and 1923 clinics dispensed legal narcotics to addicts. According to a Federal Bureau of Narcotics pamphlet, *Narcotic Clinics in the United States,* issued in 1953, a total of forty-four clinics operated during this time. All but one were closed by July of 1921. The Shreveport Clinic, in Louisiana, remained open until 1923. They were all closed, states the pamphlet, when the city and state officials responsible for the areas in which they were located discovered that they encouraged the illicit traffic in narcotics and were instrumental in spreading addiction.[3] Nothing in the pamphlet indicates that the clinics were opened at the instigation of the federal authorities.

As with all else which fails to fit their conception of

right conduct, the Bureau baldly misstated the facts about the clinics. And as we shall see, the evidence they use to support their criticism is contradicted by the historical record.

The clinics were opened on the recommendation of the Commissioner of Internal Revenue, the federal official whose responsibility it was to enforce the Harrison Act. The recommendation was contained in the Annual Report of the Commissioner for the fiscal year ending June 30, 1919:

> It is evident from the enforcement of the law as amended that provision must be made for the treatment and cure of addicts who are unable to obtain supplies of drugs necessary to meet their proper needs, as the ordinary addict, when suddenly deprived of the drug to which he is addicted, suffers extremely both physically and mentally, *and in this condition may become a menace to life and property* ... To meet immediate demands for the treatment of addicts this matter has been taken up with State and municipal boards of health, and in many instances local clinics have been established to handle this situation temporarily.[4] [italics added]

A year later, the humane common sense of this statement was no longer evident. The Annual Report of 1920 had a very different tone:

> ... During the month of July, 1919, instructions were issued to collectors of internal revenue to confer with the United States attorneys and local health authorities in their districts with a view to devising some plan whereby bona fide narcotics cases might be properly treated.
>
> As a temporary expedient to relieve this seemingly critical situation a number of narcotics clinics or dispensaries were established. Some of the so-called clinics that have since been established throughout the country without knowledge or sanction of this Bureau apparently were established for mercenary purposes or for the sole purpose of providing

145

applicants with whatever narcotic drugs they required for the satisfaction of their morbid appetites. Little or no attempt was made by some of these private clinics to effect cures, and prominent physicians and scientists who have made a study of drug addiction are practically unanimous in the opinion that such clinics accomplish no good and that the cure of narcotic addiction is an impossibility unless accompanied by institutional treatment. Steps are now being taken to close these clinics, *which are not only a menace to society but a means of perpetuating addiction.* In many cases their continued existence constitutes a flagrant violation of the law.[5] [italics added]

So, though in 1919 addicts unable to procure their drugs legally were seen as a menace to society, by 1920 the clinics created to forestall this danger were the menace. This abrupt change of attitude and reasoning cannot be explained by what happened in the clinics. They had barely begun operating, and what little evidence existed concerning the results was both too fragmentary and too contradictory to support this sudden official turnabout. The true explanation is, apparently, that the Prohibition Unit created to enforce the Volstead Act replaced the revenue collectors as the enforcers of the Harrison Act and brought their prohibition philosophy and tactics with them.[6]

As these sources clearly state, the clinics were opened at the recommendation of the federal authorities and then closed at their instigation—facts of history either ignored or contradicted in the Bureau of Narcotics' account of the clinics. As for the increase of traffic in illicit drugs attributed to the clinics, there is no historical connection whatever. The growth of illicit traffic was the direct result of the Supreme Court decisions which first made it very difficult and then almost impossible for addicts to get narcotics from private physicians. Moreover, only a very small proportion of the addict population, some 15,000, was ever registered in the clinics, hardly enough to account for the extent of the traffic. And the illicit traffic was already highly developed by 1919, before the clinics were opened. And naturally so. Once narcotics were illegal, how else could an addict supply his needs? Yet the Bureau attempts to persuade us that a return to the pre-Harrison situation, when illicit traffic was unnecessary and which the clinics on a small and constricted scale represented, contributed to the increase in the traffic!

Narcotic Clinics in the United States contains a great variety of dubious material, not the least of which is an account of the successful Shreveport Clinic. This account, written to justify the closing of the clinic, bears no discernible resemblance to the authoritative description given in Terry and Pellens' *The Opium Problem.*[7] The opening sentence of the Bureau's piece sets the tone of inaccuracy nicely:

> It was estimated that 75 per cent of the drug addicts in Texas made their headquarters at Shreveport following the operation of that clinic.[8]

The truth of the matter is that only 1,287 addicts were registered at the clinic during the whole period of its existence, and the Treasury Department itself estimated the addict population of Texas in 1919 to be 2,371.[9] Thus, even if all the patients attending the Shreveport, Louisiana clinic were Texans, the Bureau's statement is false. But of course they were not all Texans. In 1920, for example, only 331 nonresidents received narcotics at the clinic.[10]

The closing of the Shreveport Clinic made the local law enforcement people very unhappy. After it was finally shut down, the city police department and the sheriff reported increasing trouble with users and peddlers, who, they said, were creating new addicts.[11]

Admittedly, many of the clinics were badly run, and abuses certainly occurred. They were set up hastily, and few were in operation long enough to have their shortcomings corrected. Lessons, however, were learned from the failures. Unfortunately, our drug officials seemed to have learned nothing from the successes. Those which, like the Shreveport Clinic, were well-run, were discredited by the Bureau's falsehoods and propaganda. And only someone knowledgeable and open-minded enough to dig into Terry and Pellens had, by 1953, any chance of disputing the drug police assertion that the clinics were dismal failures and dislodging it from its position as the generally accepted version of the clinics' history.[12] This perhaps explains why, when in 1955 the Daniel's Subcommittee considered a plan submitted by the New York Academy of Medicine to establish narcotics clinics throughout the nation, the subcommittee was confidently able to cite among its ten propositions condemning the plan that "The legalized distribution of free drugs would create new addicts and increase the narcotics problem in the United States," and that "Experiments with similar 'narcotics clinics' in the 1920's showed their abject failure."[13]

There is no historical evidence to support the first proposition either in this country or abroad. On the contrary, as with the Shreveport Clinic, the evidence indicates that addiction and traffic increased when the clinics closed. And here in America not only did the traffic increase, but the price of drugs skyrocketed, providing further impetus to the expansion. For example, the New Haven Police Department—which ran that city's clinic—estimated that the prices of heroin and morphine doubled after the clinic was shut down.[14] And in England, as we

148

shall see, there is indisputable evidence that the current government-run clinics have reduced the illicit traffic, and more importantly, have reduced not just the growth of addiction but have reversed the trend. There are fewer heroin addicts in England today than when the clinics began operating in 1968.

As for the second proposition, it is really a question of what constitutes the standards for success or failure. Critics of the clinics usually base their arguments on the implicit assumption that they were set up to cure addicts, which was not the case. They were established, as the Commissioner of Internal Revenue plainly stated, to protect society from the dangers we all are now so familiar with—the acts against property and persons an addict must commit to acquire the high price of illicit drugs. Judged against this standard, even the badly mismanaged New York City clinic was successful. For though New York had a well-established and well-patronized illicit market, the simple existence of the clinic kept illicit drug prices at a reasonable level. So long as the clinic operated, an addict unable to meet street prices had only to register at the clinic and he would be supplied. The clinics were a powerful restraint on the greed of the peddlers. One cannot charge monopoly prices unless there is a monopoly, and the peddlers didn't enjoy this benefit until the clinics were closed down.

Not content with seriously distorting the historical record of the American clinics, the BNDD and its supporters have expended a good deal of energy and time lying about the English methods of treating addiction. Indeed, they have gone to great lengths to deny that a British system exists. The anonymous author of one document circulated by the Bureau, after attacking in slanderous fashion those who had advocated trying the British system and after citing some of the facts the advocates had put forward to justify their proposal, concluded:

> Nothing could be further from the truth. The British system is the same as the United States system.[15]

This was written in 1954 about a system which for some thirty-four years had permitted private physicians to write narcotics prescriptions for addicts!

Eight years later, Anslinger's successor, Henry Giordano, was making similar noises:

> The so-called British system has been discussed many times in this country . . . but there's really little difference between the methods actually practiced today in England and those practiced here. Dr. Granville Larimore and Dr. Henry Brill . . . went over there to study British methods . . . When they came back they said in effect that they could find very little difference between the control method used in England and here. . . .[16]

In fact the methods actually practiced in England were the same as they were eight years before: private physicians prescribing narcotics to addicts.

The British system or, as our drug police like to say, the "so-called" British system developed, ironically enough, from a basic drug law which was in all important respects the same as the Harrison Act. Like Harrison, the Dangerous Drug Laws of 1920 were passed as control and record-keeping statutes. And like Harrison, they made no mention of addiction or addicts, nor did they attempt to define what correct medical practice should be in that area. But also as with Harrison, the law enforcement officials soon took exception to doctors' prescribing narcotics to addicts. They believed, possibly because of the manner in which Harrison was being implemented in the

United States, that the Dangerous Drug Laws prohibited such actions. The Rolleston Committee was appointed in 1924 to reconcile the conflict, and in 1926 it handed in a report which, by its interpretation of the laws, settled the way in which England was to handle addicts and addiction. The report held that doctors could prescribe or administer drugs to addicts on a regular basis when "the patient, while capable of leading a useful and relatively normal life when a certain minimum dose is regularly administered, becomes incapable of this when the drug is entirely discontinued." [17] In effect the Rolleston Committee had made it England's official policy to treat addiction as a medical rather than a law enforcement problem. Physicians, not policemen, were made the arbiters of drug addiction treatment, a policy still in effect today.

Considering the fact that within a span of twenty-four years the Treasury Department and the Federal Bureau of Narcotics prosecuted some 25,000 doctors for prescribing narcotics to addicts, it seems fantastic that spokesmen for the Bureau repeatedly have claimed there was no difference between the British and American systems. And it is even more fantastic that Doctors Larimore and Brill could reach such a conclusion after visiting England and correctly stating in their report that British physicians were lawfully prescribing narcotics to addicts. Perhaps as employees of the New York State Department of Health and Mental Hygiene making a report to their chief, Governor Nelson Rockefeller, they felt they were required to reach it. But as Alfred Lindesmith has written, "The logical processes involved in reaching this conclusion have never been divulged and are not understood." [18]

Larimore and Brill also made the curious discovery "that there was no British narcotic system and there never had been such a system in the country," a discovery they made after finding "that there was no official registration, no clinic system, and no formal arrangement for official issue of narcotics to addicts." [19] Thus, because England did not have a system it never had, England did not have a system! Which is like saying either you are the person I think you should be or you are not a person—a way of reasoning which allows indefinite escape from reality.

But the doctors were apparently unable to convince themselves of their own findings, for they have since argued that the system they said did not exist prevailed because "there had never been a significant narcotic problem in that country," and thus "physicians had never lost the right to prescribe narcotics to addicts . . . " [20] This statement, besides ignoring the difficulties resolved by the Rolleston Committee Report, carries the implication that the way addicts are treated has no effect on the size of the addict population. And along the same lines they concluded "that the low incidence of addiction in Britain was attributable to the habits and customs of the country and not the result of any special methods of handling addicts." [21] Implicit in *this* conclusion is the view that the illicit traffic which always springs up when drugs aren't legally available has nothing whatever to do with spreading addiction—a view shared not even by our law enforcement officials, who have always used, as an argument for their policies, the fact that where heroin is readily available in the streets, addiction rises.

(This is a view Larimore and Brill now seem to share: on a 1965 visit to England they found that the number of known cases of heroin addiction had "increased . . . and that the increase was due to the sudden appearance of street addiction in Britain.") [22]

The Rolleston Committee Report served as the basis for England's drug policy from 1926 to 1965. (In 1961 the

Brain Committee reviewed the drug situation and concluded there was no need for change.) After 1961, however, a small number of doctors began overprescribing
heroin—one wrote six kilos' worth of prescriptions in one
year.[23] The overflow got into the streets, and the addiction rate rose. The Brain Committee was reconvened and
issued a second report on July 31, 1965, which recommended the following measures:

1   All addicts to dangerous drugs should be notified to a
    central authority.
2   To treat addicts a number of special treatment centers
    should be established, especially in the London area.
3   There should be powers for compulsory detention of
    addicts in these centers.
4   The prescribing of heroin and cocaine to addicts should
    be limited to doctors on the staff of these treatment
    centers.
5   It should be a statutory offense for other doctors to
    prescribe heroin and cocaine to an addict.[24]

With the exception of (3), the Brain Committee recommendations were accepted by the government and became
part of the Dangerous Drugs Act of 1967. Compulsory
registration of addicts went into effect in February 1968,
and by April of that year only clinic doctors could
prescribe narcotics to addicts.

Though motivated by a fear of rising addiction, the
Brain Committee never considered abandoning the long-
held policy of treating addiction as a medical problem.
They wrote:

We have borne in mind the dilemma which faces the
authorities responsible for the control of dangerous drugs in
this country. If there is insufficient control it may lead to
the spreading of addiction—as is happening at present. *If,
on the other hand, the restrictions are so severe as to
prevent or seriously discourage the addict from obtaining*

any supplies·from legitimate sources, [they] may lead to
the development of an organized illicit traffic. The absence
hitherto of such an organized illicit traffic has been attributed largely to the fact that an addict has been able to obtain
supplies of drugs legally. But this facility has now been
abused, with the result that addiction has increased.[25]
[italics added]

But almost three years went by before the recommendations were implemented, and during the interval the
overprescribing abuse continued. The number of known
heroin addicts rose from 521 in 1965 to 2,240 in 1968.[26]

As finally constituted, the clinics were not compelled
to follow any one treatment philosophy. No central
authority dictates policy. Following the principle that
addiction is a medical problem, maintenance and treatment of addicts is left to the discretion of the individual
clinic directors. They all share the view that the addict is a
patient, but their methods of handling their patients vary.
The one common trend is the gradual reduction of the
amount of heroin prescribed in each clinic—a trend that
has apparently developed as much from a competition
among the clinics to reduce their total heroin prescriptions
as from any specific treatment goals. The result has been
that now the great majority of registrants receive either
methadone alone or a combination of methadone and
heroin. But this movement towards methadone may not be
irreversible. Doctors frequently shift their patients from
one drug to another, depending on the given situation.
And with the rise of methadone addiction—most new
registrants are methadone rather than heroin addicts—
methadone may lose some of its luster.

(Contrary to the claim of most American experts that
heroin maintenance can't work because there is no way to
stabilize the dosage, the British clinics seem to have
succeeded in doing this. For example, Dr. Margaret Tripp

of St. Clement's Clinic reported that fifty percent of her patients were stabilized on a regulated dosage after one year of treatment. [27] And a Vera Institute paper, commenting on the general situation respecting stabilization, states that "... although when the clinics first began operating, large doses of heroin were prescribed (approximately 300 milligrams in an average day) addicts are now being stabilized on no more than one third of that dosage.") [28]

London, where eighty percent of England's addicts reside, has fourteen clinics. There are thirteen other specialized addiction facilities scattered throughout the country and an additional forty-two hospitals with outpatient services for addicts. In 1970 the monthly average of patients receiving heroin and/or methadone was slightly over 1,150. New admissions dropped from a monthly average of sixty-six in 1970 to forty-one in 1972. [29]

Except for the less than two percent who have severe mental problems, suffer from addiction-related medical complications, or who have no homes, addicts are not administered drugs *in* the clinics. Instead, their prescriptions, usually for one week's supply, are mailed to the druggist of their choice, who in turn furnishes the prescribed drug on a daily basis. The reason for this procedure is well-described in the Vera Institute paper:

> The British are interested in attracting *all* addicts into a regulated program and in this way keeping medical tabs on the entire problem and undercutting the growth of a large black market. The need to have an attractive "treatment lure" has been recognized since the clinics were established and explains many facets of the treatment program... It is for this reason that addicts are permitted to self-inject their drugs and to inject them outside the treatment unit. This allows the addict to regulate both the amount of heroin in each "shot" and the frequency of injecting or

155

"fixing," although the clinic doctor still controls the amount prescribed per day.[30]

Similarly, the British clinics recognize the lure of the needle: when starting an addict on methadone, they prescribe it in shootable form. The switch to oral methadone is made only if the patient agrees to it.

The doctors staffing the clinics are not content merely to maintain addicts on heroin or methadone. Their common goal is to wean their patients from narcotics. None of them, however, believes this can be done with threats or harsh sanctions. They usually attempt to transfer patients from heroin to methadone and then hopefully to a drug-free state, but if the patient is functioning well on heroin—e.g., holding a regular job—they leave well enough alone. And if after going on methadone the patient regresses, he is allowed to go back to heroin. This is one more facet of the "treatment lure" principle: giving the patient confidence that his best interests and well-being are the deciding factors, not some bureaucratic decision handed down by unseen and uncaring authority. Most important in this regard, the patient soon learns that no treatment decision is irrevocable. If he can't make it on one treatment, he will be given another. He is not threatened with dismissal from the clinic just because he can't achieve goals set by someone else. Consequently he remains in his clinic and in touch with his doctor, a fact which can hardly be stressed too much. For you cannot hope to cure an addict if you neither know who nor where he is.

Henry Brill, of Larimore and Brill, visited England again in July of 1971 and wrote "that addiction is no longer on the rise and there may have been a decrease in the last year." He added, however, that "while the overall figures are indeed encouraging, some question remains about the results of clinic treatment when judged by individual cases," citing a survey which found that among other things most clinic patients had used nonprescribed drugs during the month before the survey and that about one-third of them had been involved in criminal activities other than drug law violations. From this he concluded that, with respect to the argument for treating addiction as a medical rather than a law enforcement problem, one could "find material from either side of the well-worn polemics on narcotics and other drugs in the British story." [31]

One could, if one looked hard enough and with sufficient bias. Viewed objectively, the British approach has produced vastly better results than the American in all the major ways in which heroin addiction affects society:

Heroin addiction is declining, not rising as it is here.

The following table [32] indicates the trend,

NUMBER OF KNOWN ADDICTS, SEX, AND DRUGS USED

Year	Number of known Addicts	Sex		Drugs Used*				
		M	F	Heroin	Meth-adone	Mor-phine	Co-caine	Peth-idine
1945	367	144	223					
1950	306	158	148					
1955	335	159	176	54	21	179	6	64
1960	437	195	242	94	68	177	52	98
1961	470	223	247	132	59	168	84	105
1962	532	262	270	175	54	157	112	112
1963	635	339	296	237	55	172	171	107
1964	753	409	344	342	61	162	211	128
1965	927	558	369	521	72	160	311	102
1966	1,349	886	463	899	156	178	443	131
1967	1,729	1,262	467	1,299	243	158	462	112
1968	2,782	2,161	621	2,240	486	198	564	120
1969	2,881	2,295	586	1,417	1,687	345	311	128
1970	2,661	2,071	590	914	1,820	346	198	122]

*Alone or in combination with other drugs.

SOURCE: Drugs Branch, Home Office.

157

As the table shows, the number of known heroin addicts dropped from a high of 2,240 in 1968, to 1,417 in 1969, and to 914 in 1970. Meanwhile, however, the number of known methadone addicts has risen from 486 in 1968 to 1,820 in 1970.

British addiction statistics have been called inaccurate by the BNDD. Undoubtedly they are, but not so inaccurate as ours. Addiction not being a crime in England, it is far easier to count addicts there than here. Since England has a registration system, officials can, for example, check the addicts who enter their hospitals and prisons against the registration list. Indeed, by simply checking Brixton Prison in London they can get a very good idea of what is happening with the addiction rate. Brixton is a remand prison, similar to the Tombs in New York, and all London-area male prisoners are placed there for pretrial detention. Addicts buying in the illicit market are subject to arrest and if arrested usually end up in Brixton. According to Edgar May, Dr. James, the prison psychiatrist, says that in 1969 he saw 223 drug addicts, and it was rare that he encountered an unregistered one. A third fewer addicts entered Brixton in 1970, and of these, close to three-fourths were attending clinics prior to their arrests, as compared to three-fifths attending clinics in 1968.[33] It seems unlikely, therefore, that there is any large number of addicts unknown to the Home Office. (Only one person with whom I have talked claims there is a substantial number of unregistered addicts: Alice of Chapter IV. She said that when she first was in Southampton, in the spring of 1970, she knew ten junkies. Three months later she knew thirty or forty. And so far as she knew, none of them was registered, one reason being that "the clinics try to rehabilitate you when you register, and they didn't want to be rehabilitated. They wanted to stay junkies." Another reason was that they feared the clinics would force them to switch to methadone. How representative Alice's acquaintances were, I have no way of knowing. In any event the question is apparently moot now; the situation in 1972 is not the same as it was in 1970, when a prescription was not required for syringes. As Alice later said, "a lot we knew are probably registered now, because the last month I was there they changed the law, and now it's very hard to get works.")

But while heroin addiction is declining, methadone addiction is rising, though not at a rate equal to the heroin decline:

Registered Heroin Users		Registered Methadone Users	
1969	1,417	1969	1,687
1970	914	1970	1,820

Respecting this trend, Scotland Yard remarked in 1970:

> There has been a transference of addiction in as much as the treatment centers have succeeded in reducing the amount of heroin prescribed to addicts, thereby reducing the availability of this drug on the "illicit market." But, in doing so, they have increased the prescribing of methadone to counterbalance this reduction; consequently there is now far more methadone available on the "illicit market."[34]

The implication here that methadone is leaking to the illicit market from the clinics is unfortunate. There is little if any evidence that this is the case. Private physicians, though unable to prescribe heroin, can and do prescribe methadone. The leakage, as it was formerly with heroin, is probably from this source.

In any event the English have kept their hard-drug problem very much in bounds. Chiefly, it appears, because with free heroin available to addicts on the National Insurance, there is no incentive for large-scale traffickers.

159

High profits are the incentive, and they can't be had when the customer can always meet his needs free of charge, if he so chooses. And without the ready availability of heroin which results from large-scale trafficking, there is no way to create any substantial number of new heroin addicts.

There is very little illicit traffic in heroin.
Until 1968, when the clinics began operating, almost all of the heroin entering the illicit market came from overprescribing by doctors. The doctor who prescribed six kilos in a year has already been mentioned. This same man prescribed 150 grains to one patient on a single prescription, and then three days later one hundred grains to the same man. (A typical New York street bag contains one-third of a grain). The Brain Committee Report cites two other doctors who each issued single prescriptions for more than 166 grains. Indeed, given the small heroin-using population, overprescribing was on a large enough scale that British-made heroin was readily available on the streets. The fact that the price held steady at one pound per grain for several years substantiates this. At present, with very little leakage occurring, British-made heroin is reportedly selling for six pounds ($14.40) per grain in the black market, which makes it as expensive as New York City heroin. The lower quality Hong Kong heroin sells much more cheaply. Depending on one's source of supply, the price can be anywhere from one to three pounds per grain—which is a further indication that the illicit traffic is small and unorganized. Where there is a big illicit market, as in New York, competition keeps the prices and quality remarkably steady within a given market.

With heroin available at no cost from the clinics, it doesn't seem possible for a significant illicit market to develop. Importing and distributing heroin is a business, and like any other, it can't survive if the competition—in this case the British government—is able to undersell it outrageously.

It should be added that the present clinic system has not completely eliminated the black market, nor has it kept all clinic patients from supplementing their legal supplies with illicit products. A small number apparently buy street heroin. Most supplementation, however, appears to be with privately prescribed barbiturates and tranquilizers.

There is very little addiction-related crime in England.

Indeed, so little that there are virtually no publicized statistics on the question. Unlike New York, where police officials estimate that anywhere from twenty-five to fifty percent of all property crimes are committed by addicts, the London police do not so much as mention the issue. What little addict-related crime there is among the small unregistered heroin-using population seems confined to petty shoplifting.

The best indication of this lack of serious crime by addicts is a late-night walk through London. A New Yorker in London might be understandably a bit paranoid in the beginning, but he soon learns that he is perfectly safe. Muggers are simply not to be encountered. One can stroll through Hyde Park, alone and at three A.M., in perfect safety. Try that on for size in Central Park, if you are so foolish.

More than any other factor, the absence of addict-related crime has made the English police supporters of the clinic system. Though not always uncritical supporters— "They sustain addiction . . . there is no place in England where a drug addict can be cured"—they nevertheless admit "they would be in trouble if heroin were completely

161

outlawed."[35] In the same trouble, one supposes, as our drug police.

And it is not true that England offers no place for an addict to be cured. England has Synanon-type therapeutic communities, and the clinics attempt and sometimes do effect cures.

In contrast to American addicts, a substantial percentage of English addicts hold regular jobs.

Dr. Margaret Tripp of St. Clement's Clinic told representatives of the Vera Institute

> that one of the first things which happened to a patient after he entered treatment was that he went out and got a job. She found that by the end of the first year of treatment 42% of her patients were employed. This is significant [since] the majority of her patients were delinquent boys with little or no previous employment history.[36]

The Addiction Research Unit at Maudsley Hospital has done surveys which substantiate Dr. Tripp's employment statistics. They report that forty percent of all registered addicts are employed after one year in treatment.[37] This figure is derived from addicts reporting to an independent psychiatrist and thus is difficult to validate objectively. A system is being developed which will use national employment records to verify the job claims of addicts.

The four points just elucidated—the decline in heroin addiction, the small size of the illicit market, the absence of significant addict-related crime, and the relatively good working habits of English addicts—present a marked contrast to the situation in America. Narcotics officials in this country, however, refuse to believe that this great difference has anything to do with the differences in the way in which addict-users are treated abroad and here. Their supporters are equally adamant. Lindesmith quotes Dr. Brill on the subject: "there is no cause and effect relationship between the favorable situation which England enjoys with respect to narcotic addiction and the so-called British system."[38] But neither Dr. Brill nor other like-minded persons ever demonstrates to us the truth of this pronouncement. In the absence of such demonstration, it is reasonable to assume there *is* a cause-and-effect relationship—especially since prior to the Harrison Act, in the period when Americans could legally purchase narcotics, all but one of the four points held true for American addicts. And that one, a declining addiction rate, cannot be proved. Nor disproved. Our drug statistics from that time are far too sketchy to permit the question to be settled.

The BNDD and others who dismiss the British experience as irrelevant to America further argue that the sociology of the British addict is so different from that of the American addict that no meaningful comparisons can be made. They point to the great differences in traditions and cultures and cap their argument with the observation that unlike America, England does not have an "addiction-prone" population. Their proof of this consists in pointing to the small number of British addicts and saying that *if* the population *were* addiction-prone, the numbers would be far greater.[39] Such circular nonsense is the best they can do, however, since no one has yet been able to demonstrate the existence of an addiction-prone personality. Indeed, it is the absence of such an animal that has impressed most researchers in the field. (I rather think, though, that those who refer to "addiction-prone personality" are using the term as the pseudoscientific equivalent of "American Black." If they are, they are on equally slippery ground. As we have seen in Chapter II, it was only

163

after repeated and long exposure to readily available illicit heroin that the American blacks finally developed large numbers of addicts. Prior to Harrison, blacks were distinctly underrepresented in the addict population—just as are the black immigrants in England today.)

The argument that the British system could not work here because of the great differences between the British and American addicts carries a sheen of superficial plausibility. After all, what helps a bulldog might not help an eagle. True, it might not, but in this case the pertinent facts say otherwise. There is evidence to show that the American-type addict is a far better adjusted social entity when living under English conditions than when living under an American-style narcotics policy. In the early 1960s a number of Canadian addicts went to England to escape Canada's drug laws. These are essentially the same as our laws, and as a consequence the Canadian addict-user faces the same harsh conditions which restrict his opportunity to work, make stealing necessary, place him in constant confrontation with the police, and so on and on. A study of fifty of these Canadian addict-users, whom she treated in her London clinic, was published by the psychiatrist, Lady Frankau.[40] The pertinent details are as follows:

Sociologically, the addict-users represented three categories:

1 Ten were people from "good" families, who came to the clinic after becoming addicted in Europe or had left Canada immediately after beginning to use narcotics.

2 Thirty-one were persons with no evidence of criminal records before becoming addicted, but who engaged in criminal activities to support their habits.

3 Nine were persons with criminal records antedating their addiction.

Lady Frankau described the forty of the last two categories in a way which should be familiar:

> Few of these patients had ever worked steadily, all had been dependent on an illicit supply of drugs and none had been normal, gainfully employed members of society. Two reasons were given to explain their inability to work steadily: (a) they would not be able to earn enough money to maintain the necessary supply of drugs and (b) if they did find work their employers were informed, sooner or later, that they were drug addicts. The few who had money belonged to the upper hierarchy of the drug peddling world, but at one time or another the majority had been involved in selling drugs to support their addiction.[41]

This description could just as well be applied to a random collection of New York City addict-users. It is the pattern which perfectly fits what is known here and in Canada as the "criminal addict." What happened to them in England is instructive:

Eighteen were detoxified and were drug-free at the time Lady Frankau wrote her article.

Nineteen were receiving maintenance doses of heroin and were holding regular jobs. They were not known to their employers or fellow workers as addicts.

Seven were in trouble with the English police, mainly because of attempts to supplement their clinic dosages with illicit heroin. They were all persons with criminal records antedating their addiction.

Six were either dead or not in contact with the clinic.

Lady Frankau's report has been substantiated by a study of Canadian addicts in England made by the Addiction Research Unit in 1970, and reported by Edgar May.[42]

Of the ninety-one known to have come to England during the 1960s, the researcher was able to locate twenty-five. The following was true of them while in Canada:

One in twenty-five had worked steadily after becoming addicted.

Sixteen had committed five or more crimes, and one had a record of twenty separate offenses.

As a group they had spent twenty-five percent of their addicted years in jail.

Five had had a permanent residence for more than three years.

In England, by contrast:

Thirteen held full-time jobs and four held part-time jobs.

Twelve had never been charged with any crime, petty or major, and none committed more than four offenses.

As a group they had spent less than two percent of their addicted years in jail.

Ten had resided at their current addresses for two or more years, eight for one to two years, five for less than one year, and two were hospitalized at the time of the study.

Their experience was summed up by one of their number in this fashion:

> For once we could work and live like humans... There is less trouble from the police ... we don't constantly have to be paranoid ... there is less pressure ... there is no need to steal.[43]

Our drug police have consistently refused to learn anything from the British experience, even where it is clearly shown to be applicable to the American situation, as it is in the studies of the Canadian addicts. But fortunately some of our police officials are less anxious to protect their vested interest in the status quo. Police Commissioner Patrick V. Murphy of New York City has supported a proposal for an experimental heroin maintenance clinic.[44] And John J. Buckley, Sheriff of Middlesex County in Massachusetts, has done the same after visiting Great Britain and seeing the situation there for himself. His short article in the New York *Times* of April 14, 1972, is worth presenting:

> I have been in Great Britain and have seen a rational approach to the difficult problem of heroin addiction.
>
> There are two startling differences between the United States and the British approach. One is economic and the other medical. The result is apparent by just walking the streets (which one can safely do in Britain).
>
> Only one "company," the British Government, distributes heroin. The product is 100 percent pure and the price is low. No, the underworld cannot compete with this marketing effort.
>
> In our country a user must either be a pusher or a thief to support his habit. If a pusher, he must corrupt more and more young people to support his habit. The new customers must in turn hook others and so more and more lives are lost.* If a thief, he starts shoplifting, then house burglary, then assaulting, then armed robbery and—finally imprisonment.
>
> The British have always looked upon the drug addict as a sick person. When a few doctors abused their powers of prescribing heroin, Government-run clinics were established in 1968, fourteen in London where most addicts live. At the clinic, usually located in the psychiatric department of a local hospital, addicts must go once a week or twice a month, depending on his progress, for a discussion of his emotional problems and a renewal of his prescription.
>
> The concept that addicts must need more and more heroin to become higher and higher is false. Not only has

---

*This is not, as I have written earlier, the manner in which the vast majority of "pushers" operate, nor are "pushers" the causative agents in the spread of addiction. But this is the only serious quibble I have with Sheriff Buckley. I share his sentiments.

addiction been stabilized but the dosages have been reduced. In addition, 70 percent of English heroin addicts have been transferred to methadone... One important difference from American methadone clinics is that British doctors recognize there is "needle addiction"—the ritual of mainlining is almost as important as the drug itself.

While our number of addicts has increased from 315,000 in 1969 to 560,000 in 1971, the British policy has contained the problem at a constant 3,000.

I wholeheartedly endörse the proposal of the Vera Institute for [sic] Justice that an experimental heroin clinic begin this year.

I, too, would enjoy walking our streets safely.

Civil Commitment, Methadone, and Other Follies

We treat our users of illicit drugs as criminals, but we do not restrict our treatment to putting them in jail whenever the opportunity arises. As a moral nation we feel an obligation to lead them from the path of sin into the halls of righteousness, where they will no longer threaten our property and our persons. To this purpose we have three principal methods: therapeutic communities, civil commitment, and methadone maintenance. Ostensibly they all have one goal: the cure and rehabilitation of the addict. As one notable personage remarked, however, judge me by what I do, not what I say. And judging by what they do, I find it difficult to believe that our standard treatment programs are as much concerned with the welfare of the addict as they claim. Civil commitment is in practice no more than a euphemism for jailing. Methadone maintenance is somewhat like a used-car lot, where you trade in your old model for a newer, longer-lasting one—in this case heroin addiction for methadone addiction. The various therapeutic communities on the other hand *do* seem interested in cures, but they seem equally interested in maintaining the integrity of their particular approach. And they reach only a tiny fraction of the addict population in treatment.

The methods and philosophies of the three chief treatment techniques are quite different, but they use the same criteria to measure success. The treatment program is "successful" to the degree that its patients (1) stop using heroin, (2) stop committing crimes, and (3) become productive members of society. An addict who stopped his criminal activity and held a regular job but who continued to use heroin would be considered a treatment failure. Success, at bottom, is predicated on abstinence. And success in these terms has eluded all the currently accepted treatment methods except methadone maintenance—

which, whatever else can be said about it, is no abstinence program: methadone is an addictive narcotic powerful enough to blockade the effects of heroin.

Given the fact that abstinence is only rarely achieved, the question arises whether abstinence is either a reasonable or a desirable goal. On pragmatic grounds it appears if not unreasonable unlikely to be achieved. And whether or not it is a desirable goal is a question we have no way of settling at the moment, except by ethical predilections. For we do not know why some people become addicted and others, equally exposed, do not. With no general theory of addiction we can have no general theory of treatment. Moreover, we have no way of knowing—apart from his removal from the criminal scene and all its attendant liabilities—whether a "cured" addict will be better off than he was before treatment. What we do know is that there are many causes of addiction, and it is likely that different treatments will benefit different addicts. Our ignorance is so great in this area, however, that we have no predetermined method of matching the patient to the treatment. What Terry and Pellens wrote in 1928 on the subject of addiction "cures" still applies today:

> . . .for the most part, the treatment of this condition has not emerged from the state of empiricism. The various methods described in general indicate that the basis of the majority of them is merely separation of the patient from the drug. Very few of those who have described the details of treatment have given a rationale for their procedures but rather have outlined dogmatically the adoption of certain measures whose primary object is the withdrawal of the drug and have stated or left the reader to infer that the completion of the procedure brings about cure.[1]

This state of affairs has not in any way hindered the proliferation of drug-treatment programs: "Drug abuse treatment has blossomed into a billion-dollar national industry with an ambiguous clientele and an uncertain product."[2] Nor has the uncertainty of the product inhibited the fierce competition between the various treatment programs. It is estimated that there are some 1,500 to 2,000 drug-treatment programs in the country fighting for a larger slice of the treatment pie.[3]

At the moment and for the foreseeable future, methadone maintenance appears the clear winner in this competition. In New York City, where 135 drug-treatment programs operate, all but methadone maintenance are finding it difficult to get funds to fully maintain their present programs, let alone expand them. Phoenix House, Odyssey House, and Daytop, all therapeutic communities and the oldest programs in the city, have all been forced into various cutbacks as the city puts its money into a crash program to expand methadone maintenance.[4] In October 1969, city-sponsored methadone maintenance programs had 1,744 patients enrolled in thirteen facilities.[5] As of May 18, 1972 sixty-seven private programs administered methadone to 17,345 patients,[6] an explosive rate of increase which is expected to continue.

What is happening in New York City is happening all over the country. Federal officials estimated that in June of 1971 there were at least 20,000 people receiving methadone in the United States. By December of 1971 they estimated that the number had grown to between 40,000 and 50,000.[7] And by April of 1972 there were 434 methadone maintenance programs in the nation with an estimated enrollment of 65,000.[8]

The reason for this great growth is plain. What disturbs most people about heroin is not the attendant addiction, but what the addict does to support his habit: addict-related crime is the overriding issue, so far as the voters are concerned. And most methadone maintenance programs, particularly those sponsored by New York City and run on the Dole-Nyswander model, have reported significant reductions in criminal activity among their patients together with significant increases in regular employment. Critics have questioned the data supporting these widely publicized claims, but even granting the correctness of the criticism, there is little question that the well-run methadone programs greatly outperform all other established treatments when measured by the generally accepted goals of treatment: (1) abstinence from heroin, (2) reduction of addict-related crime, and (3) increase in employment rates. The publicity given this performance has created a methadone band wagon, and the politicians are clambering aboard. And with them comes the money.

Let us now look at the major treatment programs.

Therapeutic Communities. As of March 1970, there were between forty and fifty therapeutic communities in the country with a combined enrollment of somewhere between 4,000 and 5,000.[9] The number is probably not greater now, since most funds are being invested in methadone maintenance. They all share a common view of the addict: he is an emotionally disturbed person who feels insecure and inadequate when facing the demands of societal existence. They all attempt to restructure the character and personality of the addict so that he no longer needs drugs to face the world. They do this with three basic techniques: (1) group encounter therapy, (2) living in a highly structured community, and (3) a reward-punishment system based on simple behavioral psychology.

The group encounter is the basic tool. In most TCs the sessions have no formal leader, and professionals (such as

173

doctors and psychologists) are explicitly excluded. Ex-addicts are usually ceded the authority roles their experience confers on them. But despite the usual absence of doctors, psychologists, and other professional authorities, there is nothing egalitarian about the TCs. They are rigidly structured hierarchies in which status within the structure is the major reward. Graduation from any of the TCs requires passing through three distinct phases. First, the prospective member's motivation for entering the program is severely tested during the induction phase: he must withdraw himself from heroin (the TCs don't do this for him), often wait long hours at the induction center, and attend trial encounter sessions and the like. This all may take anywhere from two weeks to six months. After acceptance in the community as a full-time member, he enters phase two, the treatment program, where his psyche is dissected in encounter sessions and he is further tested with a scaled program of jobs within the community, beginning with menial tasks and progressing to those requiring more and more responsibility. This phase may last from one to two years or even longer. If it is successfully completed, the member enters phase three, the re-entry phase, where for a period of six months to a year he is gradually exposed to the outside world. If this is successful, he is graduated and usually gains full-time employment in his own TC or in some other drug-treatment program. Only rarely does a graduate completely leave the drug world.

Ultimately, all decisions on the member's progress are in the hands of the director and his staff. The only power of decision the member retains once he enters a TC is the decision to leave. He can be busted from encounter leader to dishwasher, and he has no right to appeal. The director decides when the member is ready to go outside the community on a pass, when and if he can date a girl, and everything else that pertains to his personal welfare. Given this rigidity and the stringent testing of the prospective members, it is not surprising that in most TCs anywhere from fifty to ninety percent of the applicants either are rejected or quit in the very early stages.[10]

Evaluating the results achieved by the TCs is difficult. The amount of hard data they provide outsiders is scanty at best. In March of 1970 there were said to be 918 persons in residence at various Phoenix Houses in New York, out of a total of 2,220 who had begun treatment during the three previous years. Only seventy-nine had graduated at the time.[11] There doesn't seem to have been any noticeable improvement since. During the same period, Odyssey House reported a "success" rate of 71.5 percent, but what this means is a mystery. According to one senior staff member, "nearly 1,000 persons have begun the program" and ninety-five have completed it.[12] Apparently the 71.5 percent figure applies to the ninety-five graduates—71.5 percent of *this* group has remained drug-free. But even this is open to question. Neither Phoenix House nor Odyssey House maintains formal follow-ups to verify that its graduates remain drug-free. Daytop has reported that 85 percent of its graduates stay clean. Again though, there is no formal verification procedure, and Daytop has even fewer graduates than the other two.[13]

(Synanon "success" is difficult to judge, since Synanon makes no effort to re-enter its members into society. Its directors maintain that Synanon offers its members "a way of life that is not futile." There is no good reason to doubt this claim, but there is also no good reason to believe that so closed a community will ever attract any large number of addicts.)

James V. DeLong, in *Dealing with Drug Abuse,* the Ford Foundation report, accurately sums up the effectiveness of the therapeutic communities:

> Looking at all the available evidence and the impressions of experts in the field, it is hard to escape the conclusion that TC's are, at best, good for a very limited number of drug addicts. As a rough guess, considering the initial rejection rates, the split rates, and the relapse rate, it would be surprising if careful evaluation showed that more than 5 percent of those who come into contact with the program are enabled to lead a reasonably drug-free, socially productive life.[14]

Civil Commitment. Civil commitment—or as one commentator has put it, uncivil commitment—is the euphemism used to describe the compulsory incarceration of addicts, or those in "imminent danger of becoming addicted," in treatment and rehabilitation centers for terms of up to seven years. The largest programs are in California and New York. In theory civil commitment is nonpunitive, though how locking someone up against his will can be nonpunitive escapes me.

The California program began in 1961, the New York program in 1963. A federal program was started in 1967. But the notion that the way to rehabilitate addicts is by forcing treatment on them has been with us a long time.

New York's Boylan Law, which became effective on April 14, 1914, had among its articles one that "provided for the commitment of habitual drug users who were defined as persons constantly using any habit-forming drug except under the direction and consent of a duly licensed physician."[15] Unlike the present-day commitment laws, the Boylan Law was not intended to be punitive. Reviewing the law three years after it was passed, a Joint Legislative Committee, of which John Boylan was a member, recommended "that the present laws providing for commitment of narcotic drug addicts to penal, correctional, or charitable institutions be amended to also permit the commitment of said addicts to the care of a reputable physician . . . . "[16] The recommendation was adopted in the Whitney Law of 1917.

A few years later, in 1924, the American Medical Association adopted a resolution which held that the prescription of narcotics to an addict outside an institution was an unethical practice even if given solely for withdrawal purposes.[17]

And in 1935 the Public Health Service began operating a narcotics hospital in Lexington, Kentucky. The program consisted of gradual withdrawal from opiates, together with vocational and psychiatric therapy. The hope was to prepare addicts for a productive life. The intake of patients was both voluntary and involuntary.[18]

There is a clear relationship between the early Lexington program and the current civil commitment programs. In the words of Dr. John C. Kramer:

> The roots of these commitment laws can be traced to the federal narcotics hospital in Lexington. In recounting the initial expectations for that institution Isbell writes . . . "Drug addicts were to be treated within the institution, freed of their physiological dependence on drugs, their basic immaturities and personality problems corrected by vocational and psychiatric therapy, after which they would be returned to their communities to resume their lives. It seems to have been tacitly assumed that this program was the answer and would solve the problem of opiate addiction. Within a year it was apparent this assumption was wrong . . . a more adequate treatment program [required] : (1) Some means of holding voluntary patients until they had reached maximum benefit from hospital treatment. (2) Greater use of probation and con-

trol ... (3) Provision for intensive supervision and after-care ... " Isbell goes on to say that the reasons why these problems were not solved were complex. "In 1961 the California Legislature enacted laws establishing a commitment program for addicts which was designed to accomplish those objectives recommended but never carried out at Lexington."[19]

Writing elsewhere, Dr. Kramer adds an ironic footnote:.

Lost in the cheers and hoopla accompanying the discussions of the (then new) California program at the 1962 White House Conference was a warning by Dr. Isbell, who had been through it all before at Lexington:

Although it has been obvious for many years that institutional treatment alone is not enough, and although we should and must provide for adequate postinstitutional treatment, we should not assume that these measures will be totally or even partially successful. We must remember that we are still lacking in much of the basic knowledge required for really definitive therapy of addiction. The new treatments [civil commitment] being advocated are empirical, and as yet have no firm basis in theory."[20]

The civil commitment philosophy has not only been with us a long time, it has for a long time received the enthusiastic support of the drug police. Some examples:

—"Harry Anslinger ... called yesterday for new legislation at the municipal level that would compel the hospitalization of narcotics addicts ... the commissioner added that he thought the legislation should brand drug addiction a communicable disease, thus isolating its victims from the community." The New York *Times,* July 2, 1951.

—The Federal Bureau of Narcotics's 1953 pamphlet, *Narcotics Clinics in the United States,* approvingly cites a retired Canadian policeman's recommendation that "addicts who are certified as such by three doctors be committed to federally operated narcotics hospitals for a period of not less than ten years. If a user were twice committed it was suggested that he be sent to an institution for life, and that he be provided with a useful avocation 'but permanently within the confines of the institution.'"[21]

—In 1955, the Daniel's Subcommittee, faithfully following the Bureau line and relying on Bureau testimony, rejected a New York Academy of Medicine plan for establishing narcotics clinics, noting among other things that "Addicts must be hospitalized, in an atmosphere free of narcotic drugs, or treatment will fail." The Subcommittee then noted that existing treatment programs cured only a small fraction of addicts and "suggested permanent confinement for these incurables, a suggestion which would entail, according to the subcommittee's own estimates, the provision of new prison facilities to accommodate at least 50,000 persons."[22]

—And here is Captain William H. Madden of the Los Angeles Police Department Narcotics Squad, espousing the 1962 California civil commitment laws: "There is absolutely no question but that a narcotic addict must be isolated from the balance of society. This is not only necessary for the treatment of the addict but more important that he be removed *[sic]* so that he cannot contaminate others with his vicious habit."[23]

That a punitive law enforcement philosophy informed the civil commitment programs of the 1960s is evident from a cursory examination of their procedures and facilities. The California laws provide for commitment in lieu of a sentence or prosecution. In addition, addicts can voluntarily commit themselves, or they can be committed by relatives or other persons "acting in good faith." ("Other persons" are usually school officials or local government personnel.) In fact, however, over ninety percent of those

179

enrolled are there involuntarily, after conviction.[24] And they spend their time in facilities indistinguishable from any other prison. California's main civil commitment center at Corona is a maximum-security affair with armed guards and barbed wire. It is run by the Department of Corrections, and, according to the former Chief of Research of the California Rehabilitation Center, "psychiatrists and psychologists have played only the most peripheral part in the program."[25]

The New York laws and procedures are essentially the same as California's. So are the facilities:

> The addict receives about as much rehabilitation as the criminal prisoner with about as much result—the recidivist rate for addicts is much higher than for criminals. Moreover the rehabilitation centers are run like prisons: There are guards, most of whom receive training for prison work—one guard for every 2 inmates; recalcitrant addicts are beaten and placed in isolation on reduced diets; inmates are sexually abused; there is no separation of the young from the old. The few rehabilitation programs that do exist are staffed by instructors and therapists who have received little or no training. For the 5,000 or so inmates in the 14 separate institutions there are only 4 psychiatrists, 16 psychologists, and 78 teachers and vocational instructors. The prison-like atmosphere has caused a large percentage of the addicts to try to escape.[26]

That treatment and rehabilitation centers should be indistinguishable from prisons and serve the function of prisons came as no surprise to the sponsors of the California and New York laws. They were designed to be. Here is a California judge explaining the intent of the laws:

> Now there is one thing about the philosophy of this bill that I think all of us ought to have crystal clear, because we sold the program to the legislature on this basis. This bill is for the enforced detention and treatment of *all* heroin addicts. Let's talk first of detention. . . . In this program, if

he is not amenable to treatment, he stays in the detention facility for the full [five or ten] years. . . . Thus, the bill provides for detention whether or not the addict shows any improvement. And this is the story we've told everybody, that *the number one objective of this measure is to get the narcotic addict off the street.* If he doesn't show improvement, he will stay off the street through continuing detention.

. . . If he doesn't show any improvement, he's going to stay right where he is in the detention facility for the full five or ten year period. *The basic objective of this measure is to get the addict off the street.* Secondarily, but of equal importance to all of us, is the objective of trying to do something for the person's addiction and then to return him to a normal way of life. None of us are overly optimistic.[27]

And speaking for New York—his message more guarded, the East being notoriously effete, but the tone unmistakable—the then-counsel to the state's Narcotics Addiction Control Commission:

The result of the commitment of so many addicts will be a significant reduction in crime in the city and state. More than that, since the contagion of addiction is spread not so much from pusher to the addiction-prone person as from the addict to the non-addict, there will be a substantial cut in new addicts.[28]

The ignorance and false hopes contained in this last statement are, unfortunately, typical of the drug bureaucracy. As is the blatant viciousness of the first.

Another indication of the punitive intent behind the civil commitment laws, and a clear sign that treatment and rehabilitation were of markedly secondary importance, is shown by the distinctions in sentencing embodied in New York's Volk-Metcalfe Bill: a felon can be committed for five years, the perpetrator of a misdemeanor for only three years. As if an addict who happens to be a felon is more in

181

need of treatment than one who has been apprehended for a lesser offense!

In both California and New York, law enforcement officials backed the civil commitment laws because they saw them as a means of imprisoning non-felon addicts for much longer periods than would have been possible under the criminal law.[29] In New York an addict who has either been convicted of or pleaded guilty to a misdemeanor or prostitution can be committed for up to three years. Under the criminal law a misdemeanor gets a maximum of one year, prostitution fifteen days. In California the commitment term runs from six months to seven years, with no distinction between those who have committed felonies and those who have committed misdemeanors. The average incarceration runs slightly more than three and one-half years.[30] And ironically, addicts who would have served felony sentences had they not been committed to the Rehabilitation Center, served less time than those who had committed only misdemeanors.[31]

The suspicion that such laws—which circumvent the usual safeguards for the rights of the accused imposed by criminal law—are used by the drug police to remove from the community those they consider undesirable for long and indefinite periods with no real intent to rehabilitate, is borne out both by what goes on in the facilities and by certain police practices. The laws in California and New York are applicable not only to addicts but to those in "imminent danger of becoming addicted." Snatching a "known" addict off the street on the pretense he was "behaving suspiciously" and then, after a cursory medical examination—"by one or two physicians who earn a large part of their income from these proceedings"—instituting commitment proceedings, is not uncommon.[32] And since the victims need not be addicted, but only "in imminent danger of becoming addicted," the examining physicians do not even have to observe known signs of addiction, such as withdrawal symptoms or a positive urinalysis. Needle marks are sufficient evidence, needle marks which can be present years after use has been stopped. As for the legal niceties, a former medical official of the California Rehabilitation Center observed that

> Frequently, following the examination, those people who have been snatched off the street, sent to a county jail "ward," examined and called "addicts" or "imminently" in danger of becoming addicted, are given the opportunity to "volunteer" for commitment. They are told . . . that if they do not volunteer for a two and a half year commitment, they will be involuntarily committed for seven. Under these conditions, most volunteer.[33]

This practice probably accounts for most of the ten percent who do "volunteer" in California.

There might conceivably be some pragmatic justification for the legal and personal abuses inflicted by the civil commitment programs, if they succeeded in rehabilitating any appreciable number of addicts. They have not succeeded. Their records in this respect are as dismal as their practices. In California a study of the first 1,209 inmates released to parole found that fifty percent of them had been returned to the institution by the end of the first year, one-third remained in good standing, and the remainder had violated parole but had not been returned to the institution, because no one could find them. At the end of three years only one in six had continuously remained in good standing.[34] But even this presents a better case than the actual situation. A later study revealed a worsening result: only twenty-five percent of those

183

released to parole were in good standing at the end of the first year. And, more important, it was discovered that

> a large proportion of those who "succeed" are not typical of the majority of the addict population. They are individuals who may have had little or no contact with opiates or were primarily users of opiate-containing syrups or tablets. This suggests that the likelihood of success for those individuals for whom the program was primarily intended, the heroin addicts, is even more remote than the statistics suggest.[35]

New York either has fared worse than California or its statistics are somewhat more honest. That is, those figures that are released. Officials of the Narcotics Addiction Control Commission speak of results in a carefully guarded way that gives almost no information. In June of 1971 the commission's research director testified that "a relatively small number of people" had graduated from its civil commitment program. Of these, twenty-five percent were currently abstaining from drugs, twenty-five percent were either back in the program or had entered other treatment programs, and fifty percent were either in jail after convictions on new drug charges or had returned to drugs.[36] How small is this "relatively small number"? Well, during the 1970 gubernatorial campaign the accusation was made that the NACC had spent $345,000,000 and cured 120 addicts. (At the end of 1970 the NACC had 10,764 addicts confined in its own facilities and an additional 10,419 in facilities it either funded or accredited.) Of this accusation, a report to the Ford Foundation politely said:

> It is difficult to know whether all these accusations are justified. But it is equally difficult to find disinterested observers who contradict them.[37]

That the special, discriminatory and punitive policy toward heroin users embodied in the civil commitment laws is precisely that is revealed by a 1968 Supreme Court dictum. In Powell v. Texas the Court considered the possibility of establishing compulsory treatment programs for alcoholics and noted—in rejecting the idea—that

> (1) there was no medical consensus as to a method of treatment that solved the problem; (2) there was no assurance that treatment facilities, if established, would cure the alcoholic; and (3) in fact, such a system might accomplish nothing more than the hanging of a new sign—reading "hospital"—over one wing of the jailhouse.[38]

This, mind you, from the same Court which had earlier stated in Robinson v. California that a narcotic addict could be involuntarily committed for purposes of treatment.[39] And *this,* mind you, when everything the Court said here in Powell v. Texas was well known at the time of Robinson (and much earlier of course) to apply equally to the treatment of heroin addicts: (1) there was no medical consensus on treatment methods; (2) there was no assurance that commitment would cure an addict—if anything, the Lexington experience clearly pointed in the other direction; and (3) the state legislatures had made it plain that they were far more interested in jailing addicts than in treating them.

Nevertheless, what was unconscionable treatment for alcoholics was acceptable treatment for heroin addicts. But then of course the large majority of addicts are black and brown—whereas the large majority of our 9,000,000 alcoholics are white.

Methadone Maintenance. The old Germany gave us morphine and heroin; the new Germany gave us methadone. Developed during World War II as a substitute for morphine and heroin, it is a synthetic opiate, analgesically somewhat more potent than morphine. And before there were methadone maintenance programs, there were methadone withdrawal programs. The Public Health Service facility at Lexington has used methadone—or dolophine, as it was then called—to detoxify addicts for more than twenty years. And addicts have used it to taper off, to alleviate withdrawal symptoms, and as a heroin or morphine substitute when these were in short supply for at least as long.

Taken intravenously, methadone produces a euphoric high similar to heroin, but junkies report that the high isn't as "good." Taken intravenously, it also affords an initial rush similar to heroin's, but again, junkies report that it isn't as "good" as the heroin rush. Taken either intravenously or orally, methadone is a highly addictive drug. Sudden abstinence induces withdrawal symptoms similar to those of heroin withdrawal: restlessness, shivering, sweating, running eyes and nose, nausea, intense abdominal pains, vomiting, and a great craving for a dose of the drug that will end the painful experience.

Since methadone and heroin are so similar, the question arises why the one should be substituted for the other. There are two reasons. The first is that methadone has received legal sanction: treatment facilities can dispense methadone; they can't dispense heroin. The second is that compared to heroin, methadone is a long-lasting drug: oral maintenance doses are good for twenty-four hours; a shot of heroin for only four to six hours. From the point of view of treatment facility administrators, therefore, methadone is a more practical drug than heroin.

Until Dr. Vincent Dole and Dr. Marie Nyswander developed the methadone maintenance technique, methadone was principally used to detoxify opiate addicts. The procedure used was the classic one: a dose large enough to prevent withdrawal symptoms is initially administered, and then gradually the dosage is reduced to zero over a period of one to two weeks. The same procedure is followed when heroin or morphine is the agent. If nothing else is done for the addict, detoxification, whether by methadone or any other opiate, is usually quickly followed by a return to addiction. Indeed, long-term addicts have traditionally detoxified themselves periodically, in order to reduce the size of their habits to economically manageable levels.

Methadone detoxification, therefore, like any other form of detoxification, is not a "cure." And methadone maintenance is not a "cure"—the heroin addict becomes a methadone addict. It is a treatment aimed at eliminating heroin hunger, stabilizing the addict's drug needs, and thus affording him the opportunity to lead a relatively normal life. In the words of Vincent Dole,

> The medical procedure, in brief, is to administer methadone once daily by mouth, in constant dose. After tolerance to the medication has been established, the dose (usually 80-120 mg/day) can be held constant, without escalation, for years. With this steady dosage the heroin hunger or craving is relieved and tolerance to narcotic effects of all opiate class narcotics (heroin, morphine, deladuid, demerol) is held at a high enough level to block their euphoriant effects. The patient does not experience euphoria, analgesia, or tranquilization from the methadone, and feels little or no euphoric reaction if he takes a shot of heroin.[40]

The Dole-Nyswander methadone maintenance treatment was developed in response to the clear failure of all established treatment programs in this country to effect the substantial betterment of any appreciable number of their patients. Dole hypothesized that long-term opiate addiction created a metabolic deficiency which could be successfully treated only by some form of replacement

187

therapy—maintenance on opiates or opiate substitutes such as methadone. Again in Dole's words:

> Laboratory and clinical studies have provided evidence that opiate abuse can generate a narcotic hunger or craving which may last for the duration of a person's life. This hunger appears to be symptomatic of a metabolic change in the nervous system, and is the physical basis of continued heroin addiction. Case histories suggest that addiction and narcotic hunger are developed at different rates depending on personal and social factors such as the availability of narcotics and the individual's response to opiates.
>
> Methadone, when properly prescribed, acts as a normalizer rather than as a narcotic. In this respect the treatment is similar to other maintenance therapies used in medical practice for treatment of patients with chronic metabolic disorders. The medical analogies are numerous—insulin for the diabetic, digitalis for the cardiac patient, diphenylhydantoin for the epileptic, etc. Patients with these chronic diseases are dependent on their medications for normal functioning. The methadone patient, who is also dependent on the daily dose of his medication for his normal functioning, is in the same medical status.[41]

Whether the metabolic deficiency hypothesis is correct or not—there is as yet little clinical evidence to support it, and some researchers are skeptical—will be of little importance insofar as the growth of methadone maintenance programs is concerned. Acceptance of the Dole-Nyswander technique rests on far less esoteric grounds. The initial research on methadone maintenance was funded because

> More effective methods of dealing with the relapsing criminal addicts obviously were needed. The basic idea in the new approach was to develop a medical treatment to permit otherwise hopeless addicts to function as normal citizens in society. *The immediate goal was to stop their criminal behavior.*[42] (italics added)

The Methadone Maintenance Evaluation Unit, headed by Dr. Frances Gearing of Columbia University, had under its surveillance as of October 31, 1970, thirteen inpatient units and forty-six outpatient units employing the Dole-Nyswander technique. The Gearing Committee found that the programs were eighty percent successful, as defined by retention in the programs. Through October 31, 1970, there had been 4,376 admissions to the program, and of these, 3,485 or eighty percent were still in treatment and therefore judged "successful" cases. But this is a somewhat misleading figure. It includes not only patients who date from the inception of the program in 1964, but 2,051 patients who were under treatment for less than one year—and the Evaluation Unit's own study showed that the attrition rate climbed as length in treatment increased: Three 500-patient groups were evaluated, and approximately twenty-three percent of the patients in each of them had been discharged from the program twenty-one months after admission, thirty-four percent of two groups thirty-three months after admission, and forty-two percent of one group forty-eight months after admission.[43] Perhaps offsetting these figures is the fact that the Dole-Nyswander programs have relatively strict standards for retention and more than eighty percent of those dropped are dropped because they violated these standards.[44] It may be then that if one uses the program's own standards

> on the retaining power of methadone, the common figure of 80 percent success errs on the high side. If, however, one argues that those standards are too stringent, excluding too many patients who are receiving worthwhile benefits from the program, the 80 percent figure may be too low.[45]

(On the other hand, the admission standards are at least equally strict, and *they* bias the results toward "success.")

The standards, or criteria for retention in the program, are four in number:[46]

1 Freedom from heroin use, measured by periodic urinalysis.
2 Decrease in antisocial behavior, measured by decrease in arrests and/or incarceration.
3 Increase in social productivity, measured by employment and/or schooling or job training.
4 Willingness of the patient to accept help for psychiatric problems or excessive use of other drugs.

On these four measures, the Gearing Committee found that:[47]

- Most patients test the methadone blockade during the first few months of treatment, but " . . . less than 1 percent have returned to regular heroin usage while under methadone maintenance treatment."
- Criminal activity decreased markedly. During the three years prior to entry into the program, the methadone patients had 120 arrests for every one hundred man-years. During the four years after entry, they had 4.5 arrests for every one hundred man-years. (And Joseph and Dole[48] studied the records of 912 patients admitted to the program over a four-and-one-half-year period and found a ninety percent decrease in criminal activity. Before admission the group had 4,500 convictions among them. After admission they had fifty-one convictions.)
- As of March 31, 1970, two-thirds of the patients still in the program were either employed, in school or active as homemakers after three months of treatment.

  Approximately twenty-six percent of the males were employed prior to entry into the program. After six months, fifty-seven percent of those still in the program were employed; after twelve months, sixty-six percent; and after forty-eight months, seventy-eight percent. (Offsetting these figures is the fact that after four years only fifty-eight percent of the inductees would still be in the program. Thus the seventy-eight percent employment rate would translate to forty-five patients employed out of a group that started with twenty-six employed. A net gain of nineteen.)

- Approximately eight percent had problems with chronic drinking, and an additional ten percent with amphetamines, barbiturates, and cocaine.

These are far more impressive statistics than any abstinence or civil commitment programs have achieved. And for far less in dollar costs. Therapeutic communities require anywhere from $3,000 to $10,000 per patient per year to operate; the New York and California civil commitment programs are estimated at $10,000 to $12,000 per patient/prisoner. Methadone maintenance comes in at $500 to $2,000 per patient, depending on the ancillary services offered. The lower figure is for outpatient clinics which dispense methadone and little else; the higher figure covers a fully supportive program of social and psychiatric counseling with as much inpatient treatment as necessary.[49] On the cost-effectiveness scale, therefore, methadone maintenance is the clear leader—another important reason why it is rapidly outdistancing all its rivals. Americans are much impressed by more clout for their dollar.

So far I have presented the methadone story from the sunny viewpoint of its advocates. There is another side to the story, however.

To begin with, the very positive results indicated by the Gearing Unit's evaluation have been rashly extrapolated by methadone proponents to apply to the whole addict-user population. For example, Dr. Harvey Gollance, administrator of the Beth Israel program, which serves as a central intake for New York City-sponsored methadone programs, has claimed that "methadone administered daily in controlled doses would allow 80 percent of all addicts now on the streets to begin self-supporting, normal lives."[50] Dr. Vincent Dole has also claimed—as have many others too numerous to mention—that methadone-maintained addicts would have "an 80 percent chance of becoming acceptable citizens."[51]

Such sweeping claims are not justified by the evaluation data. Closer inspection of the data reveals serious shortcomings in every area, including methodology. Right off, the data which served as the basis for the Gearing Unit's reports was not collected independently of the programs:

> When Dr. Gearing was asked if her committee went out and got its own information, she replied: "The evaluation committee did not go out . . . we got our reports of arrests in two places, both from the program and the police . . . Initially we did the employer business . . . We have not done it for some time." Apparently, the primary evaluation data are the unit directors' reports compiled from counselors' reports, all of whom are employees in the program.[52]

Second, and as already indicated, the employment figures are not as impressive as a quick reading of them might lead one to suppose. Given any group of one hundred male patients, twenty-six come into the program as job-holders. After four years only an additional nineteen are employed. And some of these hold jobs within the program. Exactly how many, Dr. Gearing didn't say. (The British heroin and/or methadone maintenance clinics report more impressive employment gains: approximately forty percent of their patients hold jobs after one year in treatment. And in some clinics virtually none of the patients were employed prior to entry.[53])

Third, although the Evaluation Unit claims that less than one percent of those remaining on the program resort to illicit heroin after the initial testing of the blockade, this claim is not supported by detailed data such as daily urinalysis. At best, weekly urinalysis is done, and this simply cannot be used as proof of abstinence from heroin. Furthermore, though Gearing reports that eighteen percent of those on the programs abuse alcohol, barbiturates, and amphetamines, one unit, the Brookdale Hospital Center in Brooklyn, has independently reported that the number of its patients seriously involved with drugs other than heroin, especially alcohol, is closer to fifty percent.[54] Some programs not evaluated by Gearing have even greater problems in this area. A study by the District of Columbia Narcotic Treatment Administration revealed that "60 percent of the addicts in methadone maintenance programs run by the District government continue to take illicit narcotics for months after starting regular methadone treatment."[55] Also a 1970 study of forty methadone patients in Philadelphia showed that 97.5 percent of them were supplementing their methadone with illicit narcotics. It was not said how often they did this.[56]

Fourth, though a decided drop in criminal activity and convictions is undeniable, the very fact that a patient is in a methadone program, a program enthusiastically supported by the police, artificially inflates this success. Dole himself reports that in cases where patients were arrested, "approximately half of the charges were dropped."[57] The same artificial inflation occurs with the incarceration statistics, "because of the legal and medical complications of institutionalizing the methadone-maintained addict in facilities where there are no methadone maintenance programs."[58]

And finally, and most important, the methadone advocates who make sweeping extrapolations from the Gearing data singularly fail to either mention or take into account the very striking fact that methadone maintenance has had little success in attracting the young people who make up the bulk of the addict-user population. Most programs now have a minimal age requirement of eighteen, but "the mean age of the patient population is usually between 30 and 35."[59] Just how far this is removed from the mean age of the addict-user population is made plain by an examination of New York's Narcotics Register, which, even with serious underreporting of teen-agers, shows that 55.5 percent of the city's addict-users are under twenty-five, 74.8 percent under thirty and only 25.2 percent over thirty.[60]

The "success" of the Dole-Nyswander methadone programs is further undercut by admission criteria that bar entry of the most difficult cases:

> All admissions are subject to final approval by the physician in charge of the unit. The program is open to any resident of New York City, aged 18 or over, addicted to opiates for at least two years. Patients who have a mixed addiction (barbiturates and amphetamines) are usually ineligible, as are those with severe psychiatric disorders.[61]

Moreover, since most patients in the program have been on a waiting list for one year or longer—at the end of 1970, 10,000 to 15,000 were said to be awaiting entry into the program in New York—the program is getting addicts who are probably more highly motivated than the general addict population.

And curiously, though the "success" of methadone maintenance is always stated in terms of the retention rate, methadone advocates never publicly make any connection between the retention rate and the single most important factor affecting it—namely, that methadone is a highly addictive narcotic. Once the patient becomes dependent on methadone, he must either remain on the program, or (1) go back to heroin, (2) procure black-market methadone, or (3) kick his habit. And despite these strong negative incentives to remain on the program, about one-third of all patients drop out before they reach their stabilization levels.[62]

There are several other issues the methadone advocates either ignore or play down:

Medical Side Effects:

It is claimed that no significant side-effects accompany methadone maintenance. Much depends on what one considers "significant."

- Reduction of libido and sexual potency in males. Dole says these gradually return to normal.
- Constipation, which Dole says can be treated with laxatives.
- More irritability, more performance difficulties and more negative outlook than either normal, neurotic or psychotic comparison groups. (But the study[63] did not make a comparison with an equivalent group of heroin addicts not on methadone.)
- Babies born addicted to methadone. Dole has reported that "the babies born to patients were not adversely affected by methadone,"[64] but recent evidence flatly contradicts him. Dr. Miryam Davis, a pediatric neurologist working with the District of Columbia Narcotics Treatment Administration on the problem of methadone babies, estimated that about thirty-five of the fifty babies born to mothers on methadone in Washington in 1971 "showed symptoms of withdrawal, ranging from an unusual

195

degree of restlessness and irritability to convulsions."
One baby was still convulsing three and a half months
after birth. Dr. Davis says the methadone babies
" . . . are quite difficult to manage. They are not
easier than the heroin babies and the mortality rate is
about the same."[65]

Social Complications:

- The practice of giving stabilized patients a week's
supply of methadone has led to several deaths of
young children who find it in the house and drink
it.[66]
- This same practice, along with overprescribing by
some private physicians and thefts by patients and
employees of programs, has resulted in considerable
leakage of methadone into the illicit market. A New
York *Times* survey of fourteen major American cities
found that all of them had an illicit market in
methadone.[67] And inevitably the rapid expansion of
methadone programs will aggravate this problem.
- An expanded illicit methadone market will produce
an increasing incidence of methadone o.d.'s. There is
evidence that this is already happening. In Washington, D.C. there were eight deaths directly attributed
to methadone overdose in 1971; in the first two
months of 1972 there were nine such deaths, plus
two others in which methadone was found in the
body. In New York there were thirteen deaths directly attributed to methadone overdose in 1971; in the
first two months of 1972 there were fourteen.[68]

Moral Objections:

- Many black militants maintain that methadone is
simply society's way of handling the addict-related
crime problem at the least possible expense and with
no regard for curing the addict of his addiction. Their

argument is not easy to answer. Methadone does reduce criminal activity among its patients, it does so less expensively than other treatments, and it does not cure addiction. And some see in methadone an even more insidious possibility:

Hell, man, when we was just plain junkies they only knew who we were when we got busted. *Now* they get us in those programs, *keep* us addicted, and they got your number as long as you need that shit, which is *forever*. The man's a real dog handler, you see? The program's a leash with thousands of leads, you dig? And guess who's the dogs? *Us,* baby![69]

• Law enforcement authorities and the courts are more and more frequently making it a condition for suspended sentence, probation, or parole that an addict enter a methadone program. The "realistic" argument for this is that the choice lies between having the addict in a methadone program or in jail, and that "the authorities will not *often* impose a methadone requirement on a man who would otherwise have been released."[70] (italics added)

Perhaps this is a "realistic" choice for the system, but what about the addict? What realistic choice is there between, say, five to seven years in Attica and entering a methadone program? And who with any experience with our courts and parole boards can be convinced of their fairness toward the typical black addict, a fairness that would restrain them from "often" forcing this "choice" on a man?

I find this development and the people who argue for it or excuse it on "pragmatic," "realistic," grounds thoroughly despicable. To be coerced into a life on methadone is intolerable under a Constitution which supposedly guarantees the inviolability of a citizen's civil liberties.

And to those who may argue that the realistic choice is between being addicted to heroin or being addicted to methadone, the answer is plain: If this be the case, and it probably is, then the only solution defensible in a free society is to at least allow a man his choice of addictions—legal methadone or legal heroin. The most commonly expressed moral objection is that methadone maintenance simply replaces one addiction with another. As one writer put it: "I fail to appreciate how legalized addiction is any improvement over illicit addiction."[71] Dole and Nyswander answer this in the following way: "What is new is our approach—and needs to be well understood—that methadone can be used as an anti-narcotic agent, blocking the euphorigenic action of narcotic drugs rather than substituting for them."[72]

The first writer is either ignorant of, or fails to understand, the history of narcotics use in this country since the Harrison Act, a history which amply demonstrates that the current dimensions of our heroin problem are directly attributable to the fact that heroin is illegal. Legal addiction could hardly help but be an improvement. Dole and Nyswander on the other hand seem to argue here that one of the good things about methadone is that it fails to give the user any joyous effects and thus is preferable to the illicit stuff that does. As puritanical or silly as this argument is, it is a politically sound one: a citizenry which balks at giving welfare mothers enough money to feed their children will hardly fork up the cash to keep addicts *happy*. Not even when it is explained to them that the costs would be a tiny fraction of what they are now paying for addict-related crime.

198

Dole and Nyswander's more substantive argument for the preferability of legal addiction to methadone over illegal addiction to heroin revolves around certain established and certain claimed differences between the drugs. According to them, heroin involves the user in a constant cycle of being high, being "straight", and being "sick"—a cycle which makes it very difficult for him to lead a normal, productive life. The high state is the euphoria produced by heroin; the straight state is the middle period when the user is coming down from the high but not yet feeling the absence of heroin in his system; and the sick state is the period when, the dose wearing off, the user begins experiencing withdrawal symptoms. Dole and Nyswander seem to imply that a major cause of this cycle, apart from euphoria, is heroin's relatively short duration of four to six hours, plus the "fact" that since an addict cannot be stabilized on heroin, he requires bigger and bigger doses for the same effect. They say what is needed to make the addict a socially productive person is the breaking of this cycle, the elimination of the high and sick ends of it, so that the user remains in the straight state, where he feels alert and well. Oral methadone, in proper dosage, does this by affording the user no euphoria and, with its relatively long duration (twenty-four hours), by circumventing the sick state. Moreover, the user can be stabilized on a given dosage.[73]

But the cycle of high, straight, and sick is not so much the result of the euphoric effects of heroin, but rather the result of heroin's illegality. An addict with a sufficient supply will certainly get high, but he won't get sick—he'll have enough on hand to prevent withdrawal. And most addicts I have known—and as it has been demonstrated in England—will, if they have an adequate supply of heroin, reserve their "highs" for their leisure time, shooting just enough during the day to keep straight and attend to business. This was also the general pattern among opiate addicts in this country prior to the Harrison Act.

Also, it is obvious that the effective duration of a given dose, whether it be heroin or methadone, is not an important issue, since a heroin user can shoot up a new dose with no more trouble than a diabetic. The really important issue for Dole and Nyswander is stabilization, for stabilization plays a major role in eliminating the up and down cycle. An addict on a stabilized dose can't get too high too often, or he won't have enough left over to get straight when the high wears off. If addicts can be stabilized on heroin, therefore, the methadone advocates' chief argument for the superiority of methadone over heroin as a maintenance drug would collapse. And contrary to Dole, the British clinics have demonstrated that addicts can be successfully stabilized on heroin.[74] Furthermore, on all the important indices of "success" for treatment programs, the records of the British clinics are at least as good as those of the Dole-Nyswander maintenance programs.[75] True, only about one-third of British clinic patients are on heroin, and the remainder are on methadone. But it is not methadone à la Dole. The English do not give blockade-size doses, nor do they often dispense oral methadone. They provide injectible methadone in doses sufficient to meet the patient's needs and no more. The patient shoots up and goes to work.

To sum up. We know almost nothing solid about the nature and causes of addiction. Because of this, what Terry and Pellens noted on the question of addiction cures is still true today—we have not emerged from the period of trial and error. Mostly error, unfortunately. Indeed, of the three major treatment techniques operating in the country today, only one, the therapeutic community, makes any real attempt to effect cures. The civil commitment programs are no more than alternative means of jailing the addict, offering very little treatment let alone any attempts at cure. And methadone maintenance is essentially a societal tool employed to reduce what society most fears from the addict: that criminal activity the high price of illicit heroin makes necessary. To this end we replace, often by coercion, a heroin addict with a methadone addict.

Our major programs have as their principal objective the elimination of the heroin addict's criminal behavior. Billions are spent to do this, billions spent to protect us from our own creation—the criminal addict. The most practicable, cheapest and humane solution is not seriously considered: changing the laws that *make* him a criminal.

No other Western nation has a drug problem remotely comparable to ours, but then no other Western nation with the exception of Canada has insisted on treating a medical problem as a law enforcement problem.

The Search
for a Solution

After passage of the Harrison Act, our elected and appointed officials managed, through ignorance, misrepresentations, and outright lies, to convince the public that the number of opiate addicts in the country could be significantly reduced and possibly eliminated entirely by making the addict a criminal. It was soon enough apparent, and is now overwhelmingly clear, that making the addict a criminal created a state of affairs in which the personal and medical problems of addiction became relatively insignificant. So insignificant that, rather than addiction itself being our chief concern these days, it is the product of our laws, addict-related crime, which almost totally preoccupies us. Indeed our major "treatment" programs—methadone and civil commitment—are designed to reduce addict-related crime. They are not designed to cure addiction.

The drug bureaucracy which created the present situation has itself implicitly acknowledged that addiction per se has nothing whatever to do with crime. For what they are most vigorously promoting and what they are allocating most funds to is legal addiction—methadone. They are silently admitting, therefore, what sane men have been telling them since before the Harrison Act: that making opiate use illegal was a dreadful mistake which, while doing nothing to curb addiction, would lead to problems the magnitude of which would dwarf anything hitherto experienced in the area. In the words of Rufus King, "All the billions our society has spent enforcing criminal measures against the addict have had the sole practical result of protecting the peddler's market, artificially inflating his prices, and keeping his profits fantastically high."[1]

But the inability to admit error in combination with a highly developed taste for power is the occupational disease of officialdom. Thus, though the sheer size and intractability of the heroin problem finally led them to a through-the-back-door admission that a legal narcotic was the only practical way of reducing addict-related crime, the drug bureaucrats felt it necessary to protect their righteous self-image and their power. They would neither confess they had been wrong all along, nor would they willingly relinquish their right to punish addicts. But the public was aroused, and they had to do *something* about the crime. Their solution was legalized addiction in the form of methadone maintenance, a halfway measure with advantages dear to the bureaucratic heart. First, it deprives the legal addict of the heroin high which at least partially compensates for the burden of addiction. Second, it leaves the drug police free to harass and punish those *other* addicts, while using the very fact of their illegal status to persuade the Congress to allocate whatever funds are claimed to be necessary for eradicating the fruits of that status—addict-related crime. This is a situation that, I repeat, the drug bureaucrats themselves created. Protecting one's vested interest should have some reasonable limit, but nothing in the history of our drug policy enforcers indicates either reason or reasonableness.

Of course when a long-term policy which was mistaken from its conception has disastrous results, such as our drug and Vietnam policies have had, it isn't easy for those responsible to repeal it outright. To do so means accepting responsibility for the horror and pain, the deaths and destroyed lives, the brutality and callous disregard for human values. Men who can't bring themselves to admit *any* mistake—papal infallibility being as necessary to politicians and bureaucrats as an acute insensitivity to truth—are not going to publicly confess to perpetuating murder and torture, just two of the crimes of which our drug establishment is guilty. There were 1,259 narcotics-related deaths in New York City alone in 1971, the vast majority of which are attributable to the illicit nature of heroin addiction. And what occurs daily in the facilities of the civil detention programs and in the other jails and prisons housing addicts is torture by any definition. And by any definition it is policy-inflicted torture when a junkie has to undergo withdrawal sickness because he can't meet the outrageous price of illicit heroin.

Government-sponsored methadone addiction is designed for what it cannot accomplish—the rescue of a failed policy. Legal methadone addiction can only marginally reduce addict-related crime, and in the long run it may not even have a marginal impact. For methadone is not attracting the great bulk of addict-users, the under-twenty-fives. Moreover, so long as the distribution and sale of heroin is immensely profitable, heroin will continue to be readily available at whatever price the traffic will bear. And it is the ready availability of heroin which fuels the rise in addiction. In 1971 New York City produced 70,000 new illicit addict-users.[2] In contrast, the city's methadone programs, though expanded to the point of outrunning funds and adequate facilities, added approximately 10,000 legal addicts.[3] Such figures hardly indicate the likelihood of a reduction in addict-related crime.

No one disputes the fact that addicts who are not criminals prior to their narcotics use, steal solely to support the high costs of their habits and for no other reason. It is such activity to which the term "addict-related crime" refers. It follows, then, that eliminating the criminal sanctions against narcotics use and making narcotics available to addict-users at their true and very low value would virtually eliminate addict-related crime. A very moderate habit of six bags a day under America's current laws costs a New York user up to $30 per day. The typical street bag contains about one-third grain of pure heroin. The New York user is paying $15 a grain for heroin which under England's government monopoly costs the addict fourteen cents[4] ($2.16 for 1,000 milligrams of pure heroin, and there are 64.79 milligrams in a grain). England has very little addict-related crime, and so would we at such prices. There is simply no need for criminal activity to raise such small sums.

Eliminating the criminal sanctions would also significantly reduce the recruitment rate of new addicts. As our law enforcement policy implicitly recognizes, the prime factor in spreading addiction is the ready availability of narcotics. In turn-of-the-century America there were anywhere from 500,000 to 2,000,000 opiate users in a population numbering 80,000,000. There were no street-corner dealers, but opiates were available at every corner drugstore for anyone who wanted them. And heroin is almost as easy to come by now. No one who has the price finds heroin difficult to obtain. The unconscionable profits possible in the heroin trade assure its availability. And profit is the only reason it is there. Once the government began selling heroin at its true value, one-hundredth the illicit price, no heroin dealer could possibly compete. The illicit market would cease to exist.

Repealing our law enforcement policy and thereby eliminating addict-related crime and reducing the growth rate of addiction would not solve all of our heroin problems. We would still have to decide how best to cure those addicts who can be cured, and how best to handle those who cannot be cured.

Curing Addicts. The only established treatment programs

which have seriously tried to cure addicts are the therapeutic communities, and they have been successful with only a very small number of addicts. Therapeutic communities should be retained for those they can help, but they cannot be expected to cure any significant percentage of addicts. There are, however, three relatively new techniques for treating opiate addiction—chemical antagonists, carbon dioxide therapy, and LSD therapy— two of which seem promising.

Chemical Antagonists: Only speaking loosely can one refer to these as cures for addiction. Their aim rather is to prevent the usual relapse into addiction after an addict has been successfully withdrawn from his drug. They are "drugs that prevent opiates from having any effect if the antagonists are administered before opiate injection and that precipitate withdrawal if administered after injection."[5]

Cyclazocine and naloxone are the antagonists which have been tested the longest. The former is a potent antagonist, effective when taken orally, and with a duration of more than twenty-four hours.[6] Its effective period of action, however, is apparently not long enough. Researchers found that patients soon "learned that by skipping doses they could experience the euphorogenic action of heroin the day following the last dose of cyclazocine."[7] Moreover, cyclazocine has very unpleasant side-effects which make it doubtful that many patients will find it acceptable. "The large doses of cyclazocine necessary to produce a blockade of heroin produced racing thoughts, delusions and hallucinations which were disturbing to patients."[8] It also produces nausea and apparently has addictive qualities of its own. Tolerance to its side effects are said to develop in time, but it seems doubtful that many patients would be willing to suffer them long enough to acquire tolerance.

Naloxone does not, according to the researchers, produce the anxiety and restlessness characteristic of cyclazocine. It is also said to be non-addictive. But "its duration of action was too short and its antagonistic properties could be surmounted four or five hours after it had been administered."[9] Later research found that a good heroin blockade, lasting twenty-four hours, could be obtained by administering very large oral doses.[10] Little has been said about what the side-effects of these massive doses might be.

The Addiction Research Center at Lexington has tested both cyclazocine and naloxone and does not seem optimistic about their value as antagonists. They are presently experimenting with N-methylcyclopropylnoroxymorphone, an agent which is said to be two or three times as potent as naloxone and to have a much longer duration of action. Again, nothing to my knowledge has been made public about its side-effects.

What the researchers are hoping to find is an antagonist which will block the effects of heroin for a week or even a month after administration of a single dose. Endo Laboratories has prepared an insoluble salt of naloxone suspended in oil which has a duration of more than two weeks.[11] And "Dr. Seymour Yolles . . . has used plastics as a vehicle for suspending drugs and has found that he can achieve significant levels of drug release for almost a month."[12] That is, Dr. Yolles implants in the patient a capsule which contains the antagonist and which slowly releases the antagonist into the patient's system. Once again, nothing to my knowledge has been made public about the side-effects of these two new developments.

Apart from cyclazocine, the antagonists being currently tested appear to have only minimal addictive properties. And since none of the antagonists eliminates the patient's craving for opiates, but only blockades their effects, the absence of addictive properties makes it unlikely that the short-duration antagonists will ever be effective heroin blockades. Since the patient is not bound to these antagonists and can skip his dose without suffering withdrawal symptoms—which he cannot do on addictive methadone—he will still crave opiates, and will always be tempted to skip his dose and shoot up. Past experience has shown that addicts usually succumb to such temptation. The longer-acting implantation techniques are still in the early research stage, and all that can be said about them is that, apart from whatever pharmacological difficulties they might present, there are certainly—as with the other antagonists and with methadone—substantial social and civil liberties questions to be answered. And they are essentially the same questions in all cases. The basic social issue is that since none of these methods effects cures, are they the most effective ways of eliminating addict-related crime, reducing the spread of addiction, and transforming the addict-user into a productive citizen? I have already explained in an earlier chapter why I think methadone is not the most effective means to these ends. And apart from the reputed absence of addictive properties, the same arguments apply to the antagonists. Moreover, at this stage there is no reason to believe that the antagonists will be as effective heroin blockades as methadone, nor is there any reason to believe that their medical side-effects will be any less serious than those of methadone—they may well turn out to be more so.

The major civil liberties question arises from the manner in which the courts, parole boards, and other law enforcement agencies are currently coercing addicts into methadone programs. There is no reason to believe that officials will behave differently if the antagonists become a popular control technique. No reason to believe, that is, that they will shrink from committing equally dangerous and unwarranted violations of an individual's rights.

Carbon Dioxide Therapy (CDT): The CDT discussed here is that employing the rapid coma technique developed by Dr. Albert A. LaVerne, wherein the patient inhales a seventy to eighty percent mixture of CO_2 in O_2, inducing a short-lived coma, from which he is returned by either breathing pure oxygen or air. Precisely how CDT works, the mechanism of action, is not yet fully understood. Appendix B contains Dr. LaVerne's description of it and rationale for it.

According to LaVerne, CDT has been used in one form or another for over one hundred years.[13] Pure CO_2 was first used as a surgical anesthesia, and then abandoned for newer anesthetic agents. Then a forty percent mixture was used to treat psychotics. The results were not substantiated by other researchers, and the treatment was abandoned. CDT was again used in 1937 in a thirty percent concentration to relieve anxiety states in neurotics. Whatever results were obtained could not be duplicated by others, and this too was abandoned. Then Dr. L. J. Meduna, using a thirty percent mixture, did extensive research on animals, and this research convinced him that CDT could alter behaviour. He began working with human patients, employing a technique where he put them to sleep with pure nitrous oxide and then administered thirty percent CO_2 in O_2 mixture for twenty to forty inhalations. With thirty inhalations the Meduna technique induced coma in three minutes, and the return to consciousness took another two minutes. He reported that the

211

technique produced an amelioration of anxiety or neurotic symptoms.

Other researchers, including LaVerne, in the early 1950s attempted to confirm Meduna's findings, but could not. LaVerne then studied higher concentrations of CO^2 and tried to determine "how we could elicit the therapeutic effect without producing a prolonged coma."[14] (It had been observed that the prolonged coma produced anxiety reactions in some patients that seemed worse than the symptoms being treated.) And he "discovered that by changing the concentration [to a seventy to eighty percent mixture], putting the patient to sleep very rapidly [the rapid coma technique versus the Meduna slow coma technique], made all the difference in the world clinically."[15]

LaVerne and Morris Herman reported in 1955 on an experiment in which the Meduna and LaVerne techniques were compared. They found that

> The clinical results of rapid coma technique were superior to those achieved by the Meduna technique; using the Meduna technique, 22% of a neurotic group improved clinically, whereas 50% improvement in a comparable group was achieved with rapid coma technique. Forty-seven percent of a group of 15 obsessive compulsive neuroses improved clinically when treated with rapid coma technique. Of a group of 24 schizophrenics, 33% improved clinically with rapid coma therapy. [The Meduna technique produced no clinical improvement in 7 patients with obsessive compulsive neuroses and none in 4 schizophrenics.][16]

The LaVerne-Herman study found that CDT was a relatively safe procedure, provided that the contraindications were observed. These were "severe hypertension, active pulmonary tuberculosis, cardiovascular heart disease, severe emphysema, acute allergic respiratory reaction, and respiratory or cardiovascular sensitivity to carbon dioxide and/or nitrous oxide."[17] They concluded that CDT was worthy of "further study in the exploration of new techniques and their application to psychiatric disorders."[18]

LaVerne continued working with CDT both at Bellevue and in private practice. On February 2, 1972, he gave a talk at Hahnemann Medical College in Philadelphia, where he reported that over a period of eleven years at a Bellevue clinic, he treated some 1,000 patients with CDT, including over 300 alcoholics.

> I would say that over half [the alcoholics] abstained from alcohol. Those who did not improve, I put on maintenance [one treatment per week] and about 15% of them were able to maintain sobriety indefinitely.[19]

He also reported that he had treated fifty private patients for heroin addiction: "48% remained drug-free from one to five years; 22% who had relapsed were placed on maintenance treatment once a week and remained drug-free up to five years; 30% were failures."[20]

In the Hahnemann talk, Dr. LaVerne stressed the facts that these were his private results and had not been subjected to outside evaluation, and that no controlled follow-up studies had been done.

Prior to this talk and after learning of Dr. LaVerne's work and observing treatment sessions, Dr. Lewis Mills, Associate Dean of Hahnemann and Chairman of the Research Committee of the Department of Medicine, initiated in collaboration with Dr. LaVerne a CDT pilot study with heroin addicts at Hahnemann Hospital. Beginning in December of 1971, nineteen volunteer patients, the great majority of whom had failed on other addiction treatment programs, spent seven days in the hospital, where they received CDT employing the LaVerne technique twice daily. All nineteen were detoxified in that

213

period, either from heroin or from methadone. They reported little or no withdrawal pains.[21]

When Dr. Mills presented this preliminary data on February 2, 1972, he emphasized that though CDT was clearly a very effective detoxifying agent, none of the original patients, and none of those who had subsequently entered the study, had been in treatment long enough to receive the full course of therapy (approximately three months with decreasing frequency of CDT). Consequently the study had no opportunity to develop the data to provide a statistical basis for projecting an ultimate cure rate. The study also suffered from inadequate follow-up procedures, chiefly because of a lack of funds.[22]

(The Hahnemann CDT pilot study was closed down in the spring of 1972 after the death of one patient resulted in a good deal of adverse publicity in the local newspapers. According to Dr. Mills, the death was from unknown causes. He did not think it had anything to do with CDT.)[23]

Although carbon dioxide therapy affects neuron activity and apparently because of this can alter behavior patterns, neither Dr. Mills nor Dr. LaVerne made mention of any subjective reports from patients on any unusual experience they had during treatments. But two patients in the Hahnemann study with whom I talked at some length both reported transcendental experiences similar to those some people have on LSD. "I saw God," one of them told me. The other indicated a like experience, but did not use the word "God." Both felt the experience had changed them and made them stronger. As is usual with such experiences, the patients were unable to be specific, but their subjective feelings of real change and gained strength were strongly expressed.

The presence of such feelings may be a prerequisite for

curing addiction. William James long ago wrote that the only sure cure for alcoholism seemed to be religion,[24] by which he meant that unless the alcoholic could achieve a dramatic change in his way of regarding himself and the world around him, cure was unlikely. Alcoholics Anonymous and the therapeutic communities work on this principle, and they are the only established treatment programs which effect any kind of cures.

Beyond detoxification, Dr. LaVerne's private results with heroin addicts have not, so far as I know, been duplicated by others. This may be because those administering the therapy have not been sufficiently trained in the use of what is apparently a highly sensitive technique. But whatever the reason, heroin addiction is a scourge great enough to warrant full investigation of any treatment showing any real promise to cure it. LaVerne's CDT technique should, therefore, be carefully studied by investigators fully trained in the technique, employing a research methodology which would assure scientifically valid results and which would adequately safeguard the patient's health and civil rights.

LSD Therapy: In 1952 Abram Hoffer and Humphry Osmond discovered that the LSD experience could be therapeutically beneficial to the alcoholic. Over the next five years they treated a large number of alcoholics with LSD. Their work convinced them that their early discovery was not a fluke and that one overwhelming transcendental experience could indeed be beneficial in curing alcoholism.[25] Following the announcement of their results in 1957, several other researchers investigated LSD therapy for alcoholism. Many of the studies suffered from inadequate controls, insufficient follow-up, and a lack of objective independent evaluation. To remedy these shortcomings, the National Institute of Mental Health sponsored LSD-research projects at Spring Grove State Hospital and then later at the Maryland Psychiatric Research Center. In one double-blind experiment at Spring Grove, 135 hospitalized alcoholics were given either high doses (450 micrograms) or low doses (fifty micrograms) of LSD. The selection was random. Six months later an independent evaluation team found that fifty-three percent of the high-dose group were "greatly improved," as opposed to thirty-three percent of the low-dose group. A follow-up eighteen months later revealed the differences were no longer so great: fifty-four percent of the high-dose group were still greatly improved, but now forty-seven percent of the low-dose group were too.[26] (Most authorities agree that alcoholism is about as difficult to cure as heroin addiction.)

According to Abram Hoffer,

> the one striking conclusion is that every scientist using psychedelic therapy with alcoholics found the same proportion of recoveries. Whether the experiments were considered controlled or not, about 50 percent were able to remain sober or to drink much less. This seems to be the universal statistic for LSD therapy.[27]

Reviewing the earlier results and especially the Spring Grove experiment with alcoholics, researchers at the Maryland Psychiatric Research Center thought it would be "reasonable to investigate the efficacy of the psychedelic approach with another type of individual generally refractory to therapeutic intervention—the narcotic addict."[28]

The Experiment

(All the data and quotes which follow are taken from a progress report entitled *Psychedelic (LSD) Therapy of Narcotic Addiction* by Charles Savage, M.D. and O. Lee

McCabe, Ph.D. The report was published by National Educational Consultants Inc. in 1972 under a slightly different title in *The Drug Abuse Controversy,* edited by C. Brown and C. Savage.)

Subjects: male narcotic addicts in Maryland correctional institutions who had not before participated in the narcotic outpatient clinic program and who satisfied selection criteria which included,

1 being between twenty-one and fifty years old
2 having at least eighteen months to go before expiration of sentence
3 agreeing, if paroled, to attend the already established outpatient clinic for daily urinalysis and weekly group therapy
4 granting written, informed consent to participate in the program after the nature of the treatment was fully explained.*

Inmates were then told they might or might not receive LSD as part of their treatment. Those who had met the selection criteria were put through a screening procedure in which "any inmate who showed evidence of organic brain damage, active liver disease, cardiovascular disease, or florid psychotic disturbance was excluded from the study."

Those volunteers who passed the selection and screening procedures were recommended by the researchers for an early parole hearing. And those who were granted parole were accepted into the study and assigned at random to either the treatment or control group. Control

---

*This is of very great importance. No patient or inmate in any program should be required to take LSD—or any other drug, for that matter—either against his will or without full knowledge of the possible consequences.

group parolees were required to attend the outpatient program, which consisted of weekly group therapy sessions and daily urinalysis. Treatment group parolees were admitted to the inpatient psychedelic rehabilitation unit. There were seventy-four parolees in all, thirty-seven in each group. The average age was 28.6, seventy-six percent were black, and the mean amount of formal education was 8.6 years. The average time institutionalized was 4.5 years. "None of the differences between treatment and control groups were statistically significant; likewise, the groups are equivalent on all psychometric indices including severity of disturbance and prognosis."

Treatment: Twenty-three hours of intensive psychotherapy over a five-week period, at the end of which one high dose (300-500 micrograms) of LSD was administered. Each patient was then given one more week of therapy to help him integrate the experience. After this the thirty-seven patients were assigned to the outpatient clinic as soon as they satisfied parole requirements (getting a job and obtaining acceptable living arrangements). At the outpatient clinic they, like the control group, received daily urinalysis and participated in weekly group therapy sessions.

Two patients had bad trips "from which they emerged shaken but more insightful . . . most of the patients had positive reactions to their experience." The patients uniformly held that the LSD experience provided a confrontation with one's problems rather than an escape from them. Savage and McCabe speculate that this may be the reason why none of the addicts had used LSD prior to the treatment program. Also, only one of them took illicit LSD afterwards, and "he has maintained complete abstinence from heroin for more than one year."

Results: The treatment and control groups were evaluated at six- and twelve-month intervals following discharge. At the time of the progress report sixty patients had been discharged for six months or more and thirty-five had completed the full twelve-month follow-up course.

In terms of total, verified abstinence from heroin since discharge versus nonabstinence since discharge, eleven of thirty (thirty-seven percent) in the treatment group had maintained total abstinence at the six-month mark as opposed to one in thirty (three percent) in the control group. At the twelve-month follow-up point seven of seventeen (forty-one percent) of the treatment group were maintaining total abstinence as opposed to one in eighteen (six percent) of the control group.

Savage and McCabe point out that total abstinence is a perhaps unrealistic treatment goal and should be seen as but one method of achieving adjustment to society. They therefore evaluated adjustment in a more general way, using a ten-point scale "in which each point is anchored in objectively verifiable terms at follow-up." For example, the highest rating, "10"; is defined as:

> Currently in community; never institutionalized nor absconded during follow-up period; no use of narcotics; employed during entire follow-up period.

And the lowest rating, "1", is defined as:

> Institutionalized or absconded almost immediately after treatment (during first month of follow-up period) after heavy narcotic usage; status quo at follow-up.

Points "2" through "9" "are similarly grounded in concrete adjustment situations of measurable degrees . . . " Using this scale, an independent evaluation team rated each parolee with information obtained from the narcotic clinic and the Board of Parole and Probation. At the six-month point, the mean rating for the treatment group was 6.33,

219

as contrasted with 4.43 for the control group. Twelve of the treatment group had "10" ratings, while eight of the control group had "1" ratings. At the twelve-month point the mean rating of the treatment group was 6.56, as contrasted with 3.72 for the control group. Nine of the treatment group had "10" ratings, while nine of the control group had "1" ratings.

The authors conclude, in part, that "preliminary results indicate that psychedelic therapy (as conducted in the present study in combination with a brief period of residence in a therapeutic community) offers potential for being a safe, short-term method of rehabilitating the chronic, 'hard-core' heroin addict."

It should be noted that the significantly positive results achieved by the treatment group came with but one LSD session. The scientific literature and the general fund of experience gained through widespread illicit LSD use suggest that multiple sessions for those who need them for a thorough "psychodynamic resolution" would produce an even higher degree of positive results than the single session model just described.

Savage and McCabe imply that they would like to try a multiple-session model, but they don't seem too optimistic about getting the chance: "It is unfortunate that, in light of the controversy presently enveloping psychedelic drug use and abuse, support for future research activities in this area probably will be determined more by social-political attitudes than by scientific considerations."

Handling Addicts Who Cannot Be Cured—Given our current lack of knowledge concerning the causes of addiction, we can hardly hope to effect cures for more than fifty percent of the addict-user population. Even assuming we developed an adequate theory of addiction and thus could expect to cure a greater percentage of addicts than we do now, there would still remain a large percentage who would have no desire to be cured. Providing them with methadone is neither eliminating addict-related crime nor curbing the growth-rate of addiction. Only providing them with heroin at its true value will do this. The question, therefore, is how best to do it. And there are three established methods of distributing heroin at prices that would drive the illicit heroin merchants out of business overnight.

I. Removing all restrictions on the distribution, sale, and use of narcotics. (In short, returning to the state of affairs which existed prior to the Harrison Act, when opiates could be purchased in any drugstore without benefit of a doctor's prescription.)

This proposal rests on the assumption that the best political situation is that which maximizes individual freedom. The current national drug policy certainly reduces freedom insofar as it restricts our choices.

If freedom of choice were granted in drug taking, certain responsibilities would have to follow. To begin with, thorough and honest drug education in our schools would be an absolutely necessary precondition. No one should be in the position of facing the choice of whether or not to experiment with narcotics without a complete understanding of the possible consequences. And then, though in a free society no one but the individual should have the right to decide what he will do with his life, this right cannot be absolute. Two obvious limitations come to mind. First, the decision to use addictive drugs should be reserved to adults. All important life-affecting decisions in our society are reserved to adults, and there appears to be no good reason to change this policy. Second, the user of addictive drugs can have no right to inflict specific harm on others.

These are essentially the limitations we place on the right to use alcohol. And as with alcohol, the right to use narcotic drugs would carry great responsibility. The user would be expected to assume responsibility for any drug-influenced behavior which resulted in actual harm to others. Moreover, since the user would be expected to fully understand the possible dangers inherent in certain drug-influenced behavior—e.g., driving a car when under this influence—engaging in such behavior would be severely punished. In short, the right to ingest heroin should not be extended to the point where it becomes a license to inflict damage on others.

The question of whether free citizens should have the right to use heroin is not, however, simply a philosophical one. There are the practical issues of addict-related crime and the spread of addiction to be considered. Removing all restrictions on the distribution, sale, and use of narcotics—other than those just discussed—would accomplish the elimination of addict-related crime, but it is doubtful that it would reduce the growth-rate of addiction. Heroin and other narcotics would be as available as alcohol is now, and anyone who wanted to try one or more of them could do so as easily as he takes his first drink. And for much, much less money. Moreover, heroin addiction itself is a clear limitation on an individual's freedom. To be sure, it is a self-imposed limitation, which is preferable to a government-imposed one. On balance, however, a government-imposed limitation appears best in this case—if only because heroin addiction is very difficult to cure and the ready availability of cheap heroin might well enlist a certain number of unwary persons into the addict ranks who would otherwise not be there.

If the above paragraph seems uncharacteristically uncertain, it is because I *am* uncertain on this question. On the one hand I deplore *any* government-imposed limitation on personal action; on the other I deplore any unnecessary spread of addiction. And I am not really sure which, in this specific case, is the greater of the evils.

Practically speaking, there is little chance that we will return to the pre-Harrison days. Public opinion would have to undergo a more drastic reversal than seems possible at this time. There is, however, some current support for the establishment of heroin maintenance clinics.

II. Heroin Maintenance Clinics—The current British experience with clinics plus the fact that "a substantial portion of [New York City's] heroin addicts, including some of the most crime prone, are unlikely to be reached by the simple expansion of existing treatment Programs"[29] has led the Vera Institute of Justice to formulate a proposal for an experimental heroin maintenance clinic in New York City. The same considerations led Police Commissioner Murphy to back a New York State Assembly bill that would create clinics to dispense heroin and other drugs to registered addicts under medical supervision. In doing so, he said that " . . . it's better to maintain these unfortunates on heroin than having them go out and commit crimes and victimize so many innocent people to support their habits."[30]

The Assembly Bill, introduced by Antonio G. Olivieri, would set up a system not substantially different from the British system. The Vera proposal is in intent quite different: "The project would attempt to stabilize addicts now using heroin and then, through a full range of social services transfer the addict into a regular rehabilitation program and off heroin."[31] The availability of legal heroin is seen in the Vera proposal as a lure to addicts to enter the program and thus be exposed to rehabilitation efforts.[32] After completing the program—initially set up for six months, but now apparently to be for one year[33] —the addict would be transferred to "drug-free therapeutic communities, narcotic antagonist, or methadone maintenance."[34]

In Chapter VI I have already given the reasons why I believe the British clinic system is far better than anything we now have here. The Olivieri Bill is, in my opinion, a step in the right direction. The Vera proposal on the other hand appears unworkable and even duplicitous. The failure of the therapeutic communities to effect substantial cure rates makes it unlikely that government will allocate funds to expand their capacity. Cutbacks have already been made in New York City. The strong possibility, therefore, is that "graduates" of the Vera program will have to be transferred to antagonists or methadone. Antagonists are still in their infancy, and even if they are ready in time, there is as yet no reason to believe that their side-effects will be any less harmful than those of methadone. The most likely end for Vera "graduates" then appears to be a methadone maintenance program.

In my estimation the only good that might come of the Vera program would be if, at the end of the initial experiment, the results in stabilization, employment rates, and the like were impressive enough to make our politicians understand there was no need for methadone programs. And certainly no need to transfer an addict doing well on heroin to methadone.

III. Heroin Prescribed by Private Physicians—If British-style heroin maintenance clinics can eliminate addict-related crime and curb the spread of addiction, so also can a wider system of distribution. And I can see no good reason why anyone who can demonstrate regular use of heroin should not be able to have it prescribed by a licensed physician. When this was the practice in this country and before there was even this limitation, we had a great number of opiate users, but we had no opiate "problem." That is, we neither had addict-related crime, nor did we have a vast army of unemployables. Opiate addicts, as Terry and Pellens have shown, worked regular jobs like the rest of the population.[35] The English felt they had a problem caused by overprescribing physicians and instituted a clinic system to resolve it. The problem, however, arose from the very special conditions which prevailed in England. There was a tiny addict population which the bad practices of a very few physicians could substantially affect. Moreover, during the period of private prescribing, England had no illicit heroin market. Thus physician's overprescriptions were the only means of creating new heroin users. Which they did, to the tune of 2,000 to 2,500. American conditions are very different. We have a huge illicit market. Anyone who wants to try heroin can easily procure it. And since legal heroin would eliminate the illicit market, even assuming a far larger number of overprescribing doctors than is likely to occur, the amount of heroin available for creating new users would be immeasurably less than what is now available in the streets. We would have a far smaller number of new addicts, rather than a greater number. And not only would we save the billions we lose through addict-related crime and the additional billions we spend on law enforcement, but a private physician dispensing system would be far cheaper than a clinic system. (And I assume here that government will pay the prescription fees of those unable to pay.) Since both would perform the same function, there seems no reason not to save the money.

225

Such a system would not replace our failed law enforcement policy with a medical policy. It would mean the elimination of the law enforcement policy certainly, but rather than treating narcotics use as a medical problem, we would be treating it as a moral and political issue. For we would simply be using doctors for distributing and recording the flow of heroin. Which was, in fact, the intention of the Harrison Act. And in doing so, we would be acknowledging a citizen's constitutional right to live his life as he sees fit, and not as some government or medical functionary decides he should live it.

In conclusion, it is clear that our law enforcement policy has been a costly and dismal failure. It is also clear that our drug bureaucrats have created a mess which threatens the very lives of our cities. And it is painfully clear that we, the citizens of America, have for far too long abdicated our responsibilities. We have allowed policemen to determine medical and social policies, determinations for which they are not qualified. We have done this by willingly accepting their self-declared, self-appointed, and self-serving roles as "experts" on drugs. And we have done this in the face of the overwhelming evidence of their gross incompetence. It is time we assumed our responsibilities. We never could, and surely cannot now, afford to rely on the architects of failure to rectify their errors. It is we who must use our common sense and realize that it is not the heroin addict who endangers us, but what our foolish laws force him to do. And it is time to understand that it is not the heroin addict who is the criminal, but those men who insist he is a criminal. We will not be able to bring the drug bureaucrats to the trial they so richly deserve, but we should make certain they can no longer cause us any further damage.

APPENDIX A
Pharmacology*

Heroin is produced from morphine, a natural alkaloid of opium, by treating morphine with acetic acid and other ingredients. Hence heroin's technical name—diacetylmorphine. Ten kilos of raw opium are required to produce one kilo of morphine base, which in turn yields slightly more than one kilo of heroin (the morphine plus the added ingredients). All three are analgesics (pain-killers) and euphoriants (agents producing feelings of happiness and well-being). Analgesically, heroin is two to three times more potent than morphine—it takes ten milligrams of morphine to produce the same analgesic effect as three or four milligrams of heroin. In equipotent doses their medical effects are quite similar, both producing analgesia, drowsiness, euphoria, constipation, sedation, relief of anxiety and tensions, and frequently, vomiting. In large doses, both can cause a fatal respiratory depression. In a normal, nontolerant individual a "large" dose can be one hundred to two hundred milligrams of morphine. No one has yet discovered how large a dose is fatal to addicts. They build tolerance to respiratory depression very quickly. Some have taken morphine in doses as large as four grams (4,000 milligrams) without any noticeable adverse effects. And the huge doses long-term heroin addicts are capable of shooting is legendary.

Most of what is known about the pharmacological action of heroin is derived from studies on morphine, morphine being more readily available here than heroin.

*Based on Jerome Jaffe, "Narcotic Analgesics," and "Drug Addiction and Drug Abuse," in L. Goodman and A. Gilman, *The Pharmacological Basis of Therapeutics* (4th ed.; New York: Macmillan, 1970).

Since heroin breaks down in the body to morphine at a rapid rate, the research is considered applicable to heroin when the differences in potency are taken into account. What follows, though taken from morphine research, can be read as applying to heroin. Important differences are noted.

Physical Effects: Medically, the opiates are used primarily as pain-killers, but precisely how they do this is still not fully understood. Local anesthetics relieve pain by blocking the transmission of the pain impulse from the nerves, but the opiates do not block the impulse. The patient under opiates can still accurately describe the source of his pain and its extent, but he no longer is concerned or anxious about it. He is detached. Because of this it is believed that morphine affects the part of the brain where nerve impulses are interpreted. In any event, morphine and heroin act directly on the central nervous system, and the precise mechanism of this action is still not yet fully understood, primarily because research into the operation of the central nervous system presents formidable obstacles to the investigator, and consequently knowledge of its action is far from complete.

It is often thought by laymen that long-term opiate use, and especially long-term heroin use, is very destructive to the body. This is not the case. No researcher has found evidence of organic damage resulting from morphine or heroin use. Even microscopic tissue investigation done in autopsy reveals no such damage. The physically wasted condition of some addicts is the result of their life-styles, not of their drugs. Similarly, the serum hepatitis and other infections common among heroin users are the result of unsterile syringes and contaminants in the illicit heroin they use, and not of heroin itself.

Apart from hepatitis and other infections caused by

unsterile conditions, addict-users are liable to fatal respiratory depressions from overdose—what the newspapers always call o.d.'s. But many researchers doubt that a significant number of true o.d.'s occur. Investigation too often reveals that the victim did not take more than his usual dose. It has been speculated that perhaps many of these so-called overdose deaths result from a sudden allergic reaction to heroin or to the quinine used in cutting street heroin. English heroin addicts, however, o.d. too, and most of the heroin they use is pure and uncut with quinine.

Morphine and heroin can be ingested orally; through the nasal passages (snorting); subcutaneously (skin-popping); or intravenously (mainlining). Depending on the method used, their effects differ. Subcutaneous and intravenous injection are the most common methods employed by illicit users. Taken subcutaneously, morphine reaches its *peak effect* (the maximum analgesic effect produced by a given dosage. It is generally assumed, though not demonstrated, that the euphoric peak and the analgesic peak are the same.) in thirty minutes to one hour. Its *duration* of analgesic action is four to six hours. Taken intravenously, the peak is reached sooner and seems to be greater. The duration is the same. Heroin is said to act similarly to morphine in these respects. Addict-users, however, report that the peak effect is reached more quickly with heroin. They rarely can distinguish morphine from heroin when taken subcutaneously, but almost always can when taken intravenously.

Psychoactive Effects: The opiates cause drowsiness, lethargy, and euphoria. They do not seem to cause slurred speech or any noticeable decrease in motor coordination. In addict-users and those receiving them in a medical setting for the relief of pain, they usually produce eu-

229

phoria. Most people in good health, however, respond negatively to opiates. Dysphoria, specifically mild anxiety and fear usually accompanied by feelings of nausea and vomiting are commonplace. Even those who go on to steady use often have these negative reactions on first use. Nausea and vomiting are common with established users, but they do not seem to mind this.

The euphoric effect, which among other things allows the user to ignore unpleasant conditions surrounding him, is apparently very powerful in those who have an affinity for the opiates. This effect can be analyzed in two parts. First, when an opiate is taken intravenously (the most common illicit method), there is a *rush* (the jolt given the central nervous system), which is usually described in sexual terms: "an orgasm in the stomach," "coming all over." Second, and to be had with any method of opiate ingestion, is the following *high*. It is difficult to define "high" in terms applicable to all addict-users, since there are so many different reasons why people use opiates and since no generally accepted theory of addiction has been developed. There are many different highs; the high of one user may not be the high of another. Generally, however, there is a greatly enhanced sense of well-being and a feeling of cool uninvolvement.

Tolerance is that state which develops when response to a given dose decreases with subsequent usage. Tolerance can, and does, develop without any perceptible physical dependence occurring. It can be described as the shortened duration and decreased intensity of the analgesic, sedative and other central nervous system depressant effects, and by a notable elevation in the average lethal dose. No limits on tolerance have been established as yet.

Tolerance develops very quickly. People have been worked up to a level of taking 500 milligrams of morphine a day within a ten-day span. Heroin tolerance apparently starts a bit more slowly, but follows the same course. It is not known whether tolerance increases arithmetically or geometrically. One hundred milligrams of morphine might be fatal to a nonuser, but no one knows if 200 milligrams would be fatal to a user accustomed to one hundred milligrams. Or whether 500 milligrams would be fatal to a user accustomed to 400.

Physical Dependence is that physiological state of adaptation to a drug following the development of tolerance, which results in a characteristic set of withdrawal symptoms when administration of the drug is stopped. To put it another way, once the user is physically dependent, he requires his drug to maintain "normal" functioning of his body. There is no definitive pharmacological definition of physical dependence. As done here, it is always defined operationally, by the presence of withdrawal symptoms. These include restlessness and a craving for the drug, violent yawning, watery discharges from the eyes and nose, sweating, violent chills, seminal ejaculations, fever, vomiting, diarrhea, insomnia, hypertension, loss of appetite, loss of weight and general aches and pains. The intensity of the symptoms is proportional to the level of dependence. The greater the habit, the more intense the withdrawal pains. But there is apparently a limit. After a morphine addict has developed a habit of 400 to 500 milligrams a day, higher doses will not lead to more intense withdrawal symptoms.

Morphine withdrawal begins a few hours after the duration of the last dose (four to ten hours, depending on the tolerance level of the user), reaches its peak of intensity around the second day, then declines. Most symptoms disappear within seven to ten days. Heroin withdrawal is essentially the same.

APPENDIX B

Dr. Albert LaVerne, who developed the current rapid-coma technique of carbon dioxide therapy, discusses its development and history in the following transcription of a tape recorded on March 1, 1972:

When did you start using CDT for heroin addiction?
A little over a decade ago. In New York City I worked here in my office. In Bellevue my experience with CO_2 began in 1950 in the clinic that I founded and conducted for CO_2 research. During those early years heroin was not a problem. Alcoholism was a serious problem. Then we had a lot of psychiatric disorders that were referred to me. In this clinic I treated hundreds of patients. And I conducted extensive research with control studies. Most of my cases were refractory patients who had failed at other modalities [treatments]: psychotherapy, psychoanalysis, drug therapy, shock treatment and community live-ins. So the heroin program began with private patients, not at Bellevue, because there were no heroin addicts coming in in those years: 1950 to 1961. I treated several morphine addicts in Bellevue, but the results were empirical, and there was no follow-up, so I could not infer whether it would work. It was purely empirical, my treating heroin addicts. Having worked in alcoholism, which is an addiction, I was curious to see whether it would work in heroin.
Were you using the same mixtures then?
Yes. But the technique was different. The technique was always changing, refined, and I learned more about how to use it and how to get the best clinical results for each type of case.
That was never mentioned in the Philadelphia presentation. Although I may be wrong.

Not the one you attended, but at the other ones—the scientific ones—it was clearly stressed. Pros and cons that you spoke about were discussed.

Could you go into that a bit?

Well, the pros and cons are that the modality is a very potent one, it has to be used with a very basic understanding of the nature of body function, body physiology. The physician using this modality must learn the principles of pharmacology, physiology, chemistry and electrophysiology, for the reason that he is using a substance which is so powerful. There are no blood-brain barriers with CO_2 therapy. It immediately gets into all levels of the body organs: brain, all levels of the brain . . . the old brain, the primitive brain and the new brain—as we say in the evolution of man from the lower animal. And it exerts its influence very rapidly and goes through a very profound series of changes . . . the neuron goes through a series of changes. First, it charges in the beginning state of a relation, charges the neuron. Then, when the charge builds up, it discharges and releases. And then it goes into a state called "quiescence state"—sleep state or the coma state. Then after about one-half minute, the patient has expelled the gas he has inhaled (CO_2), then the neuron, the quiescent neuron, begins to awaken, and as it awakens, it recharges. So each neuron is a very complex computer that has the capacity of storing, transmitting and receiving infinite numbers of impulses that we call efferent.

Neurons are either on or off; receiving or not receiving, right?

They have to be activated. They can be dormant. We only use ten percent of our brain cells under ordinary circumstances.

With CO_2 there is this total awakening of all the neurons?

Every neuron is excited.

233

All activated at the same time?

Every one of them. The effect of CDT on the neuron . . . there is no barrier that can keep it from entering the cell. In the old modality of the Meduna technique, it could protect itself. It could resist change. The circuits could resist. The Meduna, the old technique, was called the slow-coma and used much lower concentrations of CO_2. And he gave many, many more breaths—it was a gradual transition to unconsciousness or coma. We repeated Meduna's work in Bellevue and found we got no results clinically. None whatsoever. That's how I started CO_2 research. I went to Chicago and studied technique from the master, Professor Meduna, and spent a month with him and then brought it back to Bellevue to reproduce it, thinking we had a great thing, because we had a problem in Bellevue: there was nothing we could do for so many disorders of the mind. We conducted a research study, using the Meduna technique, which was thirty percent CO_2 and seventy percent oxygen. We got no results. We published. Because you always publish whether you get or don't get results. However, I was impressed with the fact that some of Meduna's patients got well and I wanted to know why. In fact he claimed that seventy-five percent of them got well. He being a great scientist, I felt it necessary to find out what there is in CO_2 that can produce change in the behavior and the brain function—brain physiology. So I began to experiment with different concentrations. I discovered that the mistake that Meduna had made was that the brain had the ability to fight back the introduction of his thirty percent CO_2. The slow transition to unconsciousness gave the brain the opportunity to defend itself against the aggressor, and it has a built-in capacity for survival, for defense—does it automatically. It fought back and in so doing developed a great deal of anxiety and

234

barriers which prevented the brain circuits from being re-established to normal patterns. To overcome this I more than doubled the concentration. I used a mixture of seventy-five to ninety percent CO_2, there always being at least twenty percent oxygen available to the brain.

Is that what you're using now?

Yes. And I give many fewer breaths than he did. And I give pre-oxygenation. The patient breathes five to twenty minutes of oxygen before administration of the CO_2 mixture. And he'll breathe from six to twenty breaths of CO_2 and then breathes a minute of oxygen, of pure air, in the recovery phase.

You say it's a very effective and potent treatment . . .

A very potent agent and very effective.

If a doctor wasn't properly prepared, what could go wrong with the treatment?

He can turn the brain off. He can intensify the symptoms. For example, a patient who is already anxious—as you yourself said, you had a suffocation experience in several near drownings—if the doctor is not aware of the anxiety that CO_2 induces, which it does in every patient to a degree, and if he has a *long transition between consciousness and unconsciousness,* then he's going to develop a superimposed treatment anxiety on the already existing problems that he's trying to cure. And the treatment can be worse than the cure, and that's what happened with the Meduna technique when he published his papers and wrote a book twenty years ago. The whole world of psychiatry and neurology and even psychologists and nonparamedical personnel thought that here was a great discovery. Just breathing ordinary CO_2 and oxygen—what a wonderful thing. And it's cheap and, by golly, just as wonderful. Pretty soon the reports kept coming back—worse or negative results. And CDT became obsolete and was stigmatized. In 1952 when I presented my first paper at the American Psychiatric Association in Los Angeles, I demonstrated my single-breath technique, where I could induce a state of unconsciousness just by breathing one breath of a mixture of seventy-five/twenty-five CO_2 and oxygen. And I demonstrated on a subject who was my nurse. Doctors in the audience were very skeptical and wanted to come up, and they wanted to try it. And they did. They went unconscious with one breath. And then another one came up and another, and finally after a dozen or so more doctors, there were no more volunteers in the audience. They were convinced that indeed it did work . . . that you *can* induce unconsciousness with one single breath. And I published the single-breath treatment of CO_2 therapy in 1952. That was the first rapid-coma paper that was published in the world. And then I began to use multiple single breaths—give the patient one breath, wait a few seconds, then another deep breath. Each time he went to sleep momentarily, he woke up, went to sleep and woke up. And I got better results than I did with the Meduna technique with thirty to forty breaths and a thirty percent mixture. You couldn't get a patient to breathe Meduna's technique. I took the treatment and it scared the hell out of me. I took several of them. I was thrown in a state of panic. I thought I was suffocating, dying and everything else. But it was all psychological. And so I knew what my patient was going through. So the CDT therapist should take the treatment himself to know what the patient is experiencing. Otherwise you will not be aware of the discomfort and be unable to provide understanding compassion to get the patient over the hump. The first few treatments are the difficult ones. After that, it's easy as pie.

That's the great difficulty with most LSD research. Very

*few of the researchers have ever taken the drug, and they
don't understand what the subjective experience is.
They're really unable to relate to the patient at all.*

I recommend that all doctors I teach ... as a matter of
fact I would refuse to grant to a physician my stamp of
approval that he's qualified to treat, unless he takes the
treatment and knows what it's like. As a matter of fact, it
would do him a lot of good. Because CDT and the modality that I am now using—have been using for many years—
is safe and is a tonic to even a normal person who has no
hang-ups whatsoever. It actually rejuvenates the body, the
mind, the brain—enables potentials to come out to the
surface. I have treated many patients—professionals,
artists, executives, people on all levels of society—who are
under a great deal of stress, usually stress exhaustion from
their activities and work. They come in for one treatment
a week, even one treatment a month, and it seems to act as
a regulator whereby it resets their metabolism, their physiology and their brain circuits and their chemistry at a more
efficient level of activity. It's most amazing how we can
actually turn the brain on or off. Turn the chemistry on or
turn the chemistry off. It is a very exciting area for
investigation, for understanding behavior, mind control,
brain control, thought processes, feelings, emotions . . .
*Has any physiological work been done trying to determine
why this happens?*

Nobody knows why it happens. The physiological work has
been done, and we've only scratched the surface. We know
that CDT is a nonspecific stress agent. Nonspecific means
that it's effective in a variety of conditions, disorders,
diseases. It's a stress stimulus. It is a very potent stimulat-
ing agent of the stress organs of the body. The stress
organs are the organs which enable you and me to be able
to carry on work, survive the trials and tribulations of our

daily activities—the problems which we encounter both externally and internally. In the external environment and also within the brain body itself. For example, an infection—ordinary bacterial infections—is an internal stress, caused by an invasion of a bacteria. The body organs are adaption-geared. There are triggered off into a defense series of chain reactions which produce antibodies against the bacteria, or other substances which neutralize the poisons bacteria manufacture and which can destroy the bacteria. The body has elaborate defense systems, whereby chemicals are manufactured called antibodies. Adrenaline is manufactured, which gears the body to fight in face of the enemy. And there are two ways in which the body fights. It can be flight—run away for self-preservation—or remain and fight back. So it's either flight or fight. If it fights back, then the muscles are thrown into activity by a surge of power generated by the pituitary adrenal axis, which are the two main organs of stress adaptation. The adrenal cortex secretes large amounts of adrenalin and cortisone types of substances, which give the body the capacity to successfully destroy the invader. So that's what nonspecific stress stimulus means.

CDT is a nonnarcotic, doesn't remain in the body. It's gone. So you've started a series of reactions in the body involving the stress organs—stress-adaptation organs. This is what we do know through physiological studies . . . chemical studies.

Is there any possibility of physiological damage?
Like everything else, it has to be given in moderation and in relatively small doses. Like a vaccine. A vaccine works in small, frequent injections. Like you get vaccinated against hay fever. Minute doses, given at intervals frequently, until the body builds up a capacity of fighting back and being able to develop an antidote to the poison that you are

breathing, inhaling or touching. Let's say the allergy that you are suffering from, whether it be internal or external. So CDT is a desensitizing agent in that respect. It is an axiom in medicine that you must do nothing harmful—*non nocere.* You must never damage the body. The doctor must be skilled, understand that he must use moderation, must use precisely the correct amount of breaths, the correct amount of concentration. It varies from patient to patient. It takes up to three months of teaching to turn out one skilled, qualified CDT therapist.

What occurs with improper administration?

You can overstimulate the adrenal cortex, like whipping a tired horse. If you're suffering from adrenal cortical insufficiency, then you can exhaust it if you overstimulate it. So you have to know what you're dealing with and give just the right amount of CO_2. For example, you could drink too much water and injure the body. Become waterlogged. If you take too much of a dose of antibiotic, you get a severe reaction. So what's involved here is that the patient will complain that he's not feeling better. Or a patient will complain that he's feeling worse. The doctor must consider taking him off the treatment, or maybe he ought to give a lighter treatment or maybe a heavier treatment. I could not in this discussion give you the medical aspects. It's too complicated.

All I'm trying to get at, Dr. LaVerne, is . . .

There's an optimal dose. I know what you're trying to get at. There's an optimal dose of the concentration, the administration for every patient, for every treatment. And they vary from treatment to treatment. And this is where the skill of the therapist comes in.

But further. The possible negative results—you wouldn't classify them as dangerous? ·

With the Meduna technique of the lower concentration,

there has been reported, and we have also reported, in our own research work, there have been a small number of psychotic reactions, triggered off by improper administration of the treatment of the Meduna technique. As a matter of fact as I explained to you earlier, the Meduna technique, because of its prolonged transition phase—which is stage two of anesthesia from consciousness to unconsciousness—stage two is so prolonged that it creates so much anxiety that it can trigger off an adverse reaction. You see, it isn't only stress, it's negative programming. And he's throwing the patient into a state of coma, and before he does that, he's negatively programming that patient. And so when the patient has a coma and wakes up, instead of feeling better, he will feel worse. Now the patient is not going to die, but the patient is going to get worse. So you defeat the very purpose of what you're trying to do. The treatment is worse than the disease. This is important with CDT, and that's what I mean when I say it's potent. But when used skillfully and intelligently, its effective.

What about your experience with your private patients?
Yes. Fifty cases that . . .
I think you said forty-eight percent in a three-month period were successful.
In a one-to-five-year follow-up. But, you see, this forty-eight percent were patients who remained drug-free, except for an occasional relapse, where they would experiment. They would just try to see what happens, and it turned out that as long as they continued the treatment, they felt they enjoyed the CO_2 trip. And they began to say, I'd rather gas up than shoot up. And when they shot up, having been exposed to CO_2 therapy, the experience was no longer exciting, and they couldn't get the high they used to get. As a matter of fact, it makes them sick. Many

of them would say, it made me sick. And this turned them off.

How did they feel sick? Was it physiological or psychological or a combination?

The reverse thing occurred with the alcoholics. You see, with heroin addicts, they have to take a much larger dosage to get a high or get that feeling, where with the alcoholics the reverse occurred. Relatively one or two drinks—a small amount of alcohol—would throw them into a state of stupor. Why? I haven't the vaguest notion. I don't understand why. This is a fertile field for research for investigators. There's something in the chemistry between the alcoholic and heroin addict that obviously is different. No question about that in my mind.

Have any investigations been done on why a heroin addict is sick after he's been on CDT, and he shoots up?

The word "sick" is subjective. Physically, we've examined them and physically, we don't find anything that's physically pathological from shooting up, any more than they were before treatment started.

With the Hahnemann pilot study, the figures weren't very impressive.

That was a small study. They treated many more patients since. Twice as many. I don't have those figures. But you must recognize that the Hahnemann study was not funded for a long-term study. There were no social workers who could follow-up the cases, see what kind of homes they were returning to after discharge from the hospital. They were coming back broke. We had to give them money for food, car fare, and we were not geared to do a long . . . it was primarily a detoxification and short-term study. And then we figured, let's continue outpatient and see what happens. That's why it's called a pilot study. Hahnemann didn't know what would happen. They'd never seen a treatment other than what the doctor and the officials who had come to my office had seen. Of course *they* had seen dozens of treatments and interviewed dozens of patients and families. And they spent months and months investigating this before they introduced it into Hahnemann. But they still were curious as hell to see, well, let's start with a fresh addict. Let's see what happens. Let's see how the patient reacts. And they were surprised to see that the patient said after the first treatment that the withdrawal symptoms went away. After the second treatment, it even lasted longer, the remission, and then finally, by the twenty-fourth to seventy-second hour, there was no pain whatsoever with withdrawal. And all of the patients, one hundred percent of them, were detoxified in a week. This is significant, because half the patients were methadone patients, or let's say less than half. Methadone addiction is impossible to detoxify. Just impossible, according to reports and the large studies that have been done. And maintenance . . . methadone patients, they go into a panic. The pain is unbearable. But they were detoxified with CDT in the same amount of time that the heroin addicts were detoxified. From this point of view, we have a scientific conclusion that we can draw, in a small study. One hundred percent of these patients, known addicts, positive morphine in the urine, positive withdrawal syndrome, were painlessly and fully detoxified and discharged within a week. It's a breakthrough, because if we never cured one heroin addict, or one methadone addict, but maintained them once a week on CDT, they would remain drug-free and crime-free. And if we could do this for America, then we have done something that the whole country has been hoping for. And I believe this can be done. A substantial number of our addicts, no matter how poorly motivated or well motivated, will, if given this treatment, which is a voluntary one, be able to find other avenues of vocation, other avenues of endeavor, and give up the life they've been leading, in spite of the fact that they're living in the same environment of high crime, high poverty and the culture they come from, that generated the disease. And this is why I'm very hopeful we can indeed provide one solution to the problem, and why I'm not interested in the long-term result of CDT at this time. If we do nothing more than provide phases one and two—drug-free and crime-free—then we have probably saved our country from destruction . . . from disaster.

To what do you attribute the failure of those people who don't seem to respond to the CDT treatment?

On the outpatient? Well, they all respond to detoxification. But not all have the motivation to continue treatment. Some of them don't show up. Disappear. Don't want to come back. Want to go back to the life they had lived. They'll go back and support a cheaper habit.

Do you think the CDT treatment . . .

In my private practice, thirty percent of these patients were such failures. Out and out failures.

Do you think the CDT treatment was very frightening and painful for the failures?

As I said earlier, CDT is a desensitizing modality. If properly used, it is not frightening or painful. When I say CDT, I'm talking about the rapid-coma technique. The Meduna technique was sensitizing. It made them worse, it created further symptoms—allergies, using the term "allergy" in a sensitizing, aggravating sense. None of the patients, even at Hahnemann, developed increasing fear to the treatment. They developed less and less fear.

243

APPENDIX C

Not the least of the costs the American adventure in Vietnam has incurred are the many thousands of G.I. heroin addicts. As of November 1971, there were an estimated 10,000 Vietnam veteran addict-users in New York City. Of these, some 3,500 were enrolled in various treatment programs, the great majority of them in programs sponsored by the city.

> Fewer than 200 of those in treatment can be found in Federal programs initiated by the Veterans Administration. . . . There is not one coordinated program for the treatment of all the veterans who are addicts that has an existence that is more than paper and ink. . . . For veterans who are certified as rehabilitated addicts there are no employment programs, even on paper. The city's Veterans Affairs Division has yet to place a single ex-addict on a job.
> —The New York *Times*. November 22, 1971.

One veteran and former addict recounted his experiences with heroin in Vietnam, his inquiries into how the Army was handling the situation, and his speculations on the problem. The tape from which the following transcription was made was recorded on February 7, 1972.

*   *   *

No matter how it starts, it's nearly impossible for a junkie to kick the habit in the same environment he got started in. I myself finally had to export myself to Hong Kong to be free from temptation. I went through four days of sleepiness, cramps, cold sweats and a centerless feeling that has no sanctuary. It's a curious thing. The so called pain of withdrawal, especially if you've only been using it for a year or so, is nothing compared to the ever-present despair and frustration when the habit's on you. You already know that you don't wake up feeling great any more. Your muscles are so sore and the spine so paralyzed, that it is impossible to get out of bed in the morning without a couple of hits of scag. If your money is running out, you start snorting it instead of smoking it. You don't waste so much. If you're snorting it, it's time to pick up a hypodermic needle from any black market medic supply on the street corner and start mainlining it. You won't waste anything then but yourself. You'd better be cool too and watch out for the purity. Remember, more cats die these days from overdoses than bullets. Compared to that trip, withdrawal is a snap. The discomfort is mostly physical. The problems are clear—you're too busy to be depressed. Your lower back is being eaten out by ants on the inside. The monkey's on your back. Sinuses are running quadruple time. You're feverish and cold all at once. You can't seem to get comfortable for sleeping or sitting. You're exhausted trying to find a method or a place to hide from it all. You run to the bathroom every fifteen minutes with diarrhea. But deep inside, a certain joy develops. All this crap means the pit's filling up, the madness is coming to an end for a while. You're off it after a few days, then you walk down that old familiar street to work. The street where all the pushers hang out. They still try and sell it to you. You say, forget it, *papasan,* I hate that shit. He smiles and says, never happen, G.I.. Unless you're much stronger than I, you're back on it in a couple of days. Once you've been addicted, it'll get you again overnight. It might've taken four weeks for someone to get a heroin habit, and he could stop for two weeks, but the next shot is it. You're on it all over again. It may take you three or four weeks to get the habit the first time, but after that, just a taste will start the ball rolling all over again. This is partly the reason for the traditionally low cure-rate in the U.S. At least a new junkie soldier will leave the source in Vietnam after a year or so. When he gets back to the world, the G.I. whose first experience with heroin came in Vietnam, stands a good chance of being cured. Whereas, the junkie who has already turned on back home, generally is not in a position to go anywhere but back to junk after he makes it through Synanon or a similar decompression service. Circumstances send him back to neighborhood pushers. It's just like trying to stop smoking cigarettes and then coming to the end of your first big meal. One thing leads to the other, and you want a cigarette. In Vietnam a guy might get out of a local drug program and go on perimeter guard duty. Well, hell, he's always been stoned on skag on guard. How is he going to get through something like that without some? Especially if the ARVN are pitching the dope up to the tower, whether he needs it any more or not.

Predictably, it's difficult for leaders to discover what goes on in a command far away from home. There's a built-in system to keep dirt and failures within the unit and try and solve the problems or at least sweep them under the carpet before they become an issue back home or an embarrassment to their superiors. Fortunately, the truth about heroin in Vietnam leaked out rather quickly, compared to the truth about massacres. Congressmen and Pentagon officials were demanding action months before anything would have been done if it had been left up to the military assistance command in Vietnam. Rensor sent people, Nixon sent people over there, because they didn't believe . . . I mean, they knew it was happening, and their low commanders said, ridiculous, we don't have any junkies. It seems strange that opium and the like have been around for so many years, and the defense establishment with all its resources, knows little about how to deal with these things. Of course there has been no precedent in this century for an epidemic. Still, in a world where eighty percent of all scientists in history are alive today, it's odd that only a handful of nonusers know anything at all about opiate addiction. In the beginning of 1971 something called Amnesty Program was instituted for all services in Vietnam. Later the Navy, despite being forerunners and liberal administrators of techniques, changed their program's name from Amnesty to Exemption. They felt this separates them from the Army, and that Amnesty implied a too easygoing attitude towards the drug offender.

The first Amnesty Programs worked this way: If a soldier wanted to turn himself in of his own volition and prior to being caught with drugs on him, he could go to his commander or chaplain or sergeant and be sent into the local program. Nothing would be put on his record. He would be exempt from duty for however long it took him to kick. A tranquilizer called thorazine might be administered. Thorazine would ease some of the discomfort. Originally soldiers were then sent back to their units. Many got hooked all over again. But they could only qualify for Amnesty or Exemption once. If caught again later, they faced less than honorable discharge or even military punishment.

Since that time, things have changed somewhat. I went to Washington to find out what was currently being done for Uncle Sam's junkies. Reading the newspapers, I've noticed that in the three months since I've returned, which would be June 1971, there seems to be a new approach every other day in the newspaper. Much to my surprise, I found what seemed to be genuine intelligence and concern at the Pentagon. This may well be because the subjects needing treatment in this case are Americans, not Gooks. In many cases, white Americans. It's generally admitted that if the heroin craze had been primarily a black soldier's problem, action wouldn't have been so quick in coming. In this era of Pentagon Papers, it's been hard for most of us to accept the mediocrity of mind that planned our worst war. On the other hand, I found it extremely difficult to reconcile the genuine intelligence and concern I encountered at the Pentagon with my previous experiences with the military. I wasn't exactly expecting hysteria, but I was prepared to deal with the fossilized mind I've known throughout six years in close contact with them. Perhaps it's because the addiction problem is not a case of dealing with foreigners, where military arrogance abounds. I spoke with the Army's Deputy Assistant Director for Manpower. By nature, I'm a very easygoing guy, but I think I get a much better feel for idiocy than a hard-nosed digger. I don't care so much about statistics as attitude. I'm not often fooled unless I want to be. The men I talked to within the Army and Navy appeared willing to drop preconceived notions of traditional discipline and robot reactions in order to deal openly and fairly with the problem that was as unpredictable to them as an American military defeat. This is a much different mentality than the circa '65-'71 George Jessel approach that tries to smooth over any possibility that our nation's finest use drugs. Now the services are almost vying for the greatest amount of drug abuse. Have you noticed that? The Navy would say, no, we've got more than you got. The Air Force would say, well, we're a smaller service. . . .

I had a chance to inquire as to how money is appropriated for non-weapons operations like drug rehabilitation, and was assured that it is as difficult for the Army to get additional funds to deal with addiction as it is for most of us to get a tax rebate. He explained that when you say, we need money, they say, great, you've got to have money—get it from some of your own organizations. In other words, they don't increase funding. The services know they have a drug problem wherever they have bases. The area of the installation tends to dictate what drugs they have available. In Europe the trip was mostly things like hashish and speed. But in Vietnam heroin is the news. There the Army has the greatest number of personnel . . . the Navy and the Air Force carry a much smaller fraction of the manload and thus the drug load. With fewer junkies to deal with, the smaller branches have the money and time to deal with the situation more extensively. The Navy is developing (I'm not sure this is true anymore) an elaborate psychological rehabilitation program. It seems, however, that everyone is taking their cue from Mr. Jerome Jaffey, who is Nixon's special adviser on drug abuse. He was recruited—I forget the date—and his first master stroke was to install urinalysis machinery at the major points of debarkation from Vietnam. This is a technique to check the urine of servicemen. It shows if they've had any heroin in the last three days or so. If the check is negative, it means either they have never used the stuff or they quit in time to go home. The military at present is taking great comfort in the fact that the urinalysis, popularly called Operation Goldenflow, reveals a five to six percent usage, as opposed to the thirty-five to forty percent figures suggested by Congressmen and observers like myself. Considering how few users can quit without help, this low figure Mr. Jaffey talked about is only those people who have been caught in that test, but as Admiral Rausch mentioned, and as any junkie knows, addicts are the cleverest people around. They are avoiding detection. Already there is a black market in clean piss, about thiry dollars a sample. Then they got tuned onto that, and then the corpsman had to watch you piss into the jar. They found apple juice in the machinery—the typical American substitute.

The military is not going to take responsibility for the type of user who can quit for three days to pass the test, even if he develops his predilection for smack in Vietnam and later will become a street user at home. In Washington I was told that the urinalysis was more and more being administered to people with a month or two weeks left in the country, so if they had to go in for detoxification, they would still go home or be released from the service on a date close to their real separation date. But since my visit to Washington the whole thing changed, and they started giving junkies early outs on purpose, to get them off their hands. They had planned that they would not turn any servicemen into society in the state of addiction. They would rehabilitate them at the expense of the government, give them, like group therapy. All the junkies would sit around and say, you asshole! Kind of like Alcoholics Anonymous. I don't know whether the change is because there are a lot more than they thought or whether they just decided to have a few model rehabilitation centers and just let the rest go, because they didn't want to handle the paper work.

The defense establishment *is* trying hard to deal with the addiction problem. But they are the first to admit they don't know what to do. They are trying everything they can, most of which is being suggested by nonmilitary personnel. The Navy is being advised by a group of thirty-five-year-old street junkies who have never been to Vietnam and have no idea of what goes on in the head of today's war junkie. The blind lead the blind. Yet some of it might help. But even when the men at the top get a good picture of what is happening, and what they might be able to do to help, it takes years for that intelligence to filter down to the drones and workers who implement the task in any military situation. I know in Saigon the situation is still very much cops and robbers, and even though a great many Saigon-based military police are themselves users, arrests are high. I asked one M.P. who was on scag how he could pull over in his jeep and bust somebody for possession, when he had the same shit in his pocket. He said it made him feel real bad, but there was sort of a quota system. And his commander had assured them all that unless narcotic arrests were high, like body counts, the ax would fall on the heads in the company. Right out front! Bust or be busted. I have a lot of information about another soldier who was arrested carrying heroin. He was withdrawn from his habit and given a forty-five automatic instead. He showed a certain zeal and hatred for the people whom he felt had got him hooked—bar girls and the like. As an alternative to being prosecuted, he would go out and set up large buys and bust as many people as he possibly could. Many of his comments about junkies, pushers and the Vietnamese, displayed deep psychosis and vengeance in his personality. But this guy was given carte blanche to run through Gomorrah and make conversions with his fiery forty-five.

Considering the situation that created most users in Vietnam, the act of having to turn to the military for help has its own little destruction. I'm not suggesting that one waits to be court-martialed rather than turn within the system for help. Even though a junkie knows best about his own folly, he's often helpless to correct what he knows. But there should be no delusion about the quality of the help the military is able to give. They are still ignorant and unqualified to get to the real source of the problem. As a scam while in the service to avoid federal prison or suicide, Amnesty is a good thing to go with. But the junkie in the end always has to solve his own problem. No one but himself is influential or powerful enough to do it for him. It doesn't necessarily have to be cold turkey. I found it a crude way, that smaller and smaller doses of a Chinese medicine—little pills containing about twenty percent tincture of opium—helped a great deal in coming off. I would take four the first day and three the next and so on, until on the last day, I had the last fraction of a single pill. When it was all gone, I still had to climb around for a few days, but the medicine had removed me somewhat from the disintegrating trip of scoring twice a day. The peculiar pressure of heroin was off my soul. This time, I stayed off.

* * *

The military undoubtedly were not qualified to treat heroin addicts. It now appears that they are unwilling as well. The withdrawal of large numbers of troops under Nixon's Vietnamization program is apparently also being used to rid the Army of its addict population:

> The United States Army in Vietnam is discharging large numbers of heroin users despite pledges from President Nixon and the Pentagon to keep drug addicts in the Army for special help and rehabilitation.
> Between 1,000 and 2,000 G.I.'s are being discharged each month, according to an official source, after having been twice certified as heroin users on the basis of urinalysis and after their commanding officers have asserted that they had not made an effort to break the habit and were of 'negligible value to the United States Army.' (The New York Times, December 19, 1971)

One assumes they were not of "negligible value" when they were needed to fight the Viet Cong and North Vietnamese. But now that they are being replaced with bombers, they are as expendable as Vietnam itself. And so it goes.

FOOTNOTES

Introduction

1. The New York Times, (The Week in Review, p.3), Oct. 24, 1971.
2. Joseph A. Greenwood, *Estimating Number of Narcotic Addicts,* Bureau of Narcotics and Dangerous Drugs, SCID-TR-3.
3. U.S. News & World Report, April 3, 1972, p. 38.

Heroisch: Large, Powerful

1. Dr. P. G. Kritikos and S. P. Papadaki, "The history of the poppy and of opium and their expansion in antiquity in the eastern Mediterranean area," United Nations, *Bulletin on Narcotics,* Vol. XIX, No. 3, July-September, 1967.
2. Ibid.
3. The material in this paragraph and the following two is taken from chapters 22 and 23 of G. Nye Steiger, *A History of the Far East,* (New York: Ginn and Company, 1944).
4. Charles Terry and Mildred Pellens, *The Opium Problem,* (Bureau of Social Hygiene, 1928), Chapter I.
5. Committee of Concerned Asian Scholars, *The Opium Trail,* 1971.
6. Richard R. Lingeman, *Drugs from A to Z: A Dictionary,* (New York: McGraw-Hill Book Company, 1969), p. 99.
7. Taped interview with New York Police Department narcotics officers, November 1, 1971.
8. Terry and Pellens, op. cit., p. 6.
9. United Nations, *Bulletin on Narcotics,* Vol. XVII, No. 1, January-March, 1965, p. 46.
10. United Nations, *Bulletin on Narcotics,* Vol. XXIII, No. 3, July-September, 1971, p. 34.
11. Peter Arnett, interview in *University Review,* October, 1971.
12. Ibid.
13. Congressman Robert H. Steele, New York Law Journal, December 6, 1971, p. 43.
14. Ibid.
15. Taped interview with returned veteran who had been addicted to heroin in Vietnam, February 7, 1972.
16. Robert H. Steele, op. cit.
17. Stewart Alsop, Newsweek, May 24, 1971, p. 108.
18. A view expressed by Anslinger in his report, as U.S. Commissioner of Narcotics, to the UN Commission on Narcotic Drugs, *Report of the Ninth Session* (1954), E/CN.7/283, p. 22.
19. Peter Arnett, op. cit., and UN Commission on Narcotic Drugs, *Report of the Fifteenth Session* (1960), E/CN.7/395, p. 15.
20. The New York Times, August 5, 1969.
21. UN Commission on Narcotic Drugs, *Report of the Twenty-First Session,* (1966), E/CN.7/501, p. 31.

22. This is a 1954 quote found in 18 above. But see UN Commission on Narcotic Drugs, *Report of the Fifteenth Session,* (1960), E/CN.7/395, p. 18.
23. UN Commission on Narcotic Drugs, *Report of the Fifteenth Session,* (1960), E/CN.7/395, p. 18.
24. Ibid., p. 15.
25. Hans J. Spielmann, The New York Times, May 17, 1972.
26. Ibid.
27. Especially Peter Dale Scott, "Heroin Traffic: Some Amazing Coincidences," *Earth,* March, 1972. But also consult listings in Bibliography under Browning and Garrett, Kamm, Adams and McCoy, McAlister, and Thayer.
28. New York Post, June 2, 1972.
29. Ibid.
30. Ibid.
31. Hans J. Spielman, op. cit.
32. Ibid.
33. Joe Fort, *The Pleasure Seekers: The Drug Crisis, Youth and Society,* (New York: Grove Press Inc., Evergreen Black Cat Edition, 1970), p. 62.
34. *The Opium Trail,* op. cit., p. 50.
35. Interview with BNDD agent, November 1, 1971.
36. New York Post, June 1, 1972.
37. *The Opium Trail,* op. cit., p. 8.
38. United Nations, *Bulletin on Narcotics,* Vol. XXIII, No. 3, July-September, 1971, p. 32.
39. Forbes Magazine, April 1, 1970, p. 20.
40. New York Times, September 25, 1969.
41. Interview with BNDD agent, November 1, 1971.
42. Forbes Magazine, op. cit., p. 20.
43. New York Times, November 21, 1971.
44. United Nations, *Bulletin on Narcotics,* Vol. XXIII, No. 3, July-September, 1971, p. 34.
45. Information on the heroin traffic flowing from Turkey to New York was obtained from interviews with agents working in the international section of the BNDD, *Dealing With Drug Abuse, A Report to the Ford Foundation, Forbes Magazine* of April 1, 1970, and a great number of newspaper stories, the listing of which would be an exercise in scholastic futility, since all the specific information is open to dispute in any case.
46. New York Times, November 16, 1971.
47. Ibid.
48. Taped interview with New York Police Department narcotics officers, November 2, 1971.
49. *Dealing with Drug Abuse* and the *Forbes Magazine* piece have slightly different figures for this progression, but a BNDD agent I interviewed on November 1, 1971, gave these figures and from what I've heard from heroin dealers in New York City they seem accurate enough.
50. U.S. News & World Report, April 3, 1972, p. 38.
51. Taped interview with New York Police Dept. narcotics officers, November 2, 1971.

52. New York Times, January 26, 1972.
53. *The Non-Medical Use of Drugs,* Interim Report of the Canadian Government's Commission of Inquiry, (Baltimore: Penguin Books Inc., 1971), p. 151.

The Wonderful World of the BNDD

1. Samuel Feinberg, *Women's Wear Daily,* December 3, 1971, p. 7.
2. Patrick V. Murphy, *New York Law Journal,* December 6, 1971, p. 40.
3. John F. Holahan, "The Economics of Heroin," in *Dealing with Drug Abuse, A Report to the Ford Foundation,* (New York: Praeger Publishers, 1972). (Hereafter cited as Holahan).
4. Charles Terry and Mildred Pellens, *The Opium Problem,* (Bureau of Social Hygiene, 1928), p. 2. (Hereafter cited as Terry and Pellens).
5. Ibid. p. 28.
6. Lawrence Kolb and A. G. DuMez, "The Prevalence and Trend of Drug Addiction in the United States and Factors Influencing It," *Public Health Reports,* 39, No. 21 (May 23, 1924), p. 8.
7. Terry and Pellens, op. cit., Chapter I.
8. Jerry Mandel, "Problems with Official Drug Statistics," in *Drug Abuse Law Review* (1971), Note 49, pp. 624-25.
9. Kolb and DuMez, op. cit., p. 20.
10. Alfred R. Lindesmith, *The Addict and the Law,* (New York: Vintage Books, 1965), p. 111.
11. Ibid., p. 110.
12. Ibid., p. 105-106
13. Bureau of Narcotics and Dangerous Drugs, *Fact Sheets,* (Washington, D.C.: U.S. Government Printing Office, 1970), p. 12.
14. *A Federal Source Book: Answers to the Most Frequently Asked Questions about Drug Abuse,* (Washington, D.C.: U.S. Government Printing Office, 1971), p. 22.
15. Ibid.
16. Joseph A. Greenwood, *Estimating Number of Narcotic Addicts,* Bureau of Narcotics and Dangerous Drugs, SCID-TR-3.
17. Ibid.
18. Holahan, op. cit., p. 287.
19. U.S. News & World Report, April 3, 1972, p. 38.
20. Ibid., p. 39.
21. Department of Health, the City of New York, *Narcotics Register Statistical Report—1969.* (Hereafter cited as *Narcotics Register*).
22. Conversation with Narcotics Register staff member, Flora Brophy, March 8, 1972.
23. The New York Times, March 16, 1972, p. 52.
24. Narcotics Register, Table I.
25. Conversation with Flora Brophy, March 8, 1972.
26. The Village Voice, October 28, 1971, p. 10.
27. Holahan, op. cit., p. 285.
28. The Village Voice, op. cit.
29. Conversation with Flora Brophy, March 8, 1972.

30. Holahan, op. cit., p. 291.
31. Ibid., p. 271.
32. Terry and Pellens, op. cit., p. 11-25, 470-471.
33. Ibid., p. 475-76.
34. Ibid., p. 25-28.
35. Ibid., p. 488
36. Ibid.
37. Ibid., p. 27.
38. J.R. Black, "Advantages of Substituting the Morphia Habit for the Incurably Alcoholic," *Cincinnati Lancet-Clinic*, XXII, (1889).
39. Narcotics Register, Table IV.
40. Ibid., Table II.
41. Ibid., Table III.
42. Ibid., Tables V through IX.
43. Lindesmith, op. cit., p. 131.
44. Ibid., Chapter I.

The Addict Personality

1. Lawrence Kolb, *Drug Addiction: A Medical Problem*, (Springfield, Ill.: Charles C. Thomas, 1962), p. 38.
2. Ibid.
3. Robert S. DeRopp, *Drugs and the Mind*, (New York: Grove Press, Evergreen Black Cat Edition, 1957), p. 150.
4. J.L. Chapel and D.W. Taylor, "Drugs for Kicks", in *1 Drug Abuse Law Review* (1971), p. 53.
5. Chapel and Taylor, op. cit., p. 54.
6. Patricia M. Wald and Peter Barton Hutt, "The Drug Abuse Survey Project: Summary of Findings, Conclusions and Recommendations," in *Dealing with Drug Abuse, A Report to the Ford Foundation*, (New York: Praeger Publishers, 1972), p. 5.
7. *The Non-Medical Use of Drugs*, Interim Report of the Canadian Government's Commission of Inquiry, (Baltimore: Penguin Books Inc., 1971), p. 157.
8. Ibid.
9. L. Lasagna, J.M. von Felsinger, H.K. Beecher, "Drug-induced mood changes in man," Journal of the American Medical Association, 157, (1955), p. 1006-1020.
10. John F. Holahan, "The Economics of Heroin," in *Dealing With Drug Abuse, A Report to the Ford Foundation*, (New York: Praeger Publishers, 1972), p. 271.
11. DeRopp, op. cit., p. 158.
12. William Butler Eldridge, "Myths and Facts," in *The Addict*, ed. Dan Wakefield, (Greenwich: Fawcett Publications, Inc., 1963), p. 61.
13. Marie E. Nyswander, "The Methadone Treatment of Heroin Addiction," *Hospital Practice*, April, 1967, unpaged reprint.
14. Ibid.
15. *Taxation of Marihuana: Hearings before the Committee on Ways and Means, U.S. House of Representatives*, 75th Cong., 1st Session, April and May, 1937, p. 24.

16. *Illicit Narcotics Traffic: Hearings before the Subcommittee on Improvements in the Federal Criminal Code of the Committee of the Judiciary,* U.S. Senate, 84th Cong., 1st Sess., pursuant to S. Res. 67, Causes and Treatment of Drug Addiction (Washington D.C.: U.S. Government Printing Office, 1955-56), Part 9, p. 4193.

17. Task Force Report: *Narcotics and drug abuse. Annotations and consultants papers.* The President's Commission on Law Enforcement and Administration of Justice. (Washington, D.C.: U.S. Government Printing Office, 1967).

18. Edward Bloomquist, *Marijuana the Second Trip* (rev. ed.), (Beverly Hills: Glencoe Press, 1971), p. 45.

19. Ibid., p. 133.

20. Ibid., p. 135.

21. Ibid.

22. Kenneth E. Newman, "Heroin, Marijuana: A Socio-Legal Analysis," in *1 Drug Abuse Law Review* (1971), p. 559.

23. *The Non-Medical Use of Drugs,* Interim Report of the Canadian Government's Commission of Inquiry, (Baltimore: Penguin Books Inc., 1971), p. 124, 158.

24. New York Times, March 21, 1972.

25. Vincent P. Dole, The Harvey Lecture, given at Rockefeller University, January 20, 1972.

26. Ibid.

27. Charles Winick, "The Addict Psychology," in *The Addict,* ed. Dan Wakefield, (Greenwich: Fawcett Publications, Inc., 1963), p. 53.

28. G.H. Stevenson, *Drug Addiction in British Columbia,* (Vancouver: University of British Columbia, 1956).

29. Nyswander, op. cit.

With Alice Through the Looking Glass

1. Joseph A. Greenwood, *Estimating Number of Narcotic Addicts,* Bureau of Narcotics and Dangerous Drugs, SCID-TR-3.

2. *The Non-Medical Use of Drugs,* Interim Report of the Canadian Government's Commission of Inquiry, (Baltimore: Penguin Books Inc., 1971), p. 44.

3. I. Chein, D.L. Gerard, R.S. Lee, E. Rosenfeld, and D.M. Wilner, *The Road to H,* (New York: Basic Books, 1964), p. 237-240, 243, 26-27.

4. Ibid., p. 243.

5. Ibid., p. 242.

6. Ibid., p. 238.

7. Ibid., p. 22, 23.

8. Taped interview, recorded November 22, 1971.

The Addict and the Law

1. Charles Winick, "Maturing Out of Narcotic Addiction," Bulletin on Narcotics, XIV, No. 1 (1962).

2. *The Non-Medical Use of Drugs,* Interim Report of the Canadian Government's Commission of Inquiry, (Baltimore: Penguin Books Inc., 1971), p. 155.

3. Arthur Light and Edward Torrance, *Opium Addiction,* (New York: Archives of Internal Medicine, 1929), Vol. 43-44.

4. J. Ball and J. Urbaitis, "Absence of Major Medical Complications Among Chronic Opiate Addicts," in J. Ball and C. Chambers (eds.), *The Epidemiology of Opiate Addiction in the United States,* (Springfield, Ill.: Charles C. Thomas, 1970), p. 306.

5. S. Irvin, *Drugs of Abuse: An Introduction to their Actions and Potential Hazards,* (Student Association for the Study of Hallucinogens, 1970), pp. 3-4.

6. Chein, D.L. Gerard, R.D. Lee, E. Rosenfeld, and D.M. Wilner, *The Road to H,* (New York: Basic Books, 1964), p. 358.

7. Charles Terry and Mildred Pellens, *The Opium Problem,* (Bureau of Social Hygiene, 1928).

8. Rufus King, *The Drug Hang-up—America's Fifty Folly,* (New York: Norton, 1972).

9. Alfred R. Lindesmith, *The Addict and the Law,* (New York: Vintage Books, 1965), p. 4.

10. Ibid.

11. Ibid.

12. The Harrison Act, 38 Stat. 785 (1914) as amended 26 U.S.C.

13. Ibid.

14. U.S. v. Jim Fuey Moy, 241 U.S. 394 (1915).

15. Webb v. U.S., 249 U.S. 96 (1919).

16. Jim Fuey Moy v. U.S., 254 U.S. 189 (1920).

17. U.S. v. Behrman, 258 U.S. 280 (1922).

18. Alfred R. Lindesmith, "Federal Law and Drug Addiction," in *Social Problems,* Vol. VII, No. 1, Summer, 1959, p. 49.

19. Ibid., p. 50.

20. Lester D. Volk, Speech in the House of Representatives, January 13, 1922, (Washington, D.C.: Government Printing Office, 1922), p. 3.

21. Lindesmith, op. cit., p. 50.

22. Ibid.

23. Ibid.

24. Linder v. U.S., 268 U.S. 5 (1925).

25. Ibid.

26. Ibid.

27. U.S. v. Anthony, 15 F. Supp. 533 (1936).

28. Commission on Public Health, N.Y. Academy of Medicine, *39 Report on Drug Addiction—II,* (1963), p. 432.

29. Cited in Lindesmith, *The Addict and the Law,* op. cit., p. 141.

30. Terry and Pellens, op. cit.

31. Rufus King, op. cit.

32. Lindesmith, *The Addict and the Law,* op. cit., p. 12.

33. Ibid., p. 13.

34. Charles E. Terry, "Narcotic Drug Addiction and Rational Administration," *American Medicine,* 26 (San., 1920).

35. Volk, op. cit., p. 9.
36. Ibid., p. 11.
37. Lindesmith, *The Addict and the Law,* op. cit., p. 260.
38. Ibid., p. 247.
39. Ibid., p. 248.
40. Ibid.
41. Ibid., p. 250.
42. Taped interview with New York Police Dept. narcotics officers, November 2, 1971.
43. U.S. News & World Report, April 3, 1972, p. 36.
44. H.J. Anslinger and W.F. Tompkins, *The Traffic in Narcotics,* (New York: Funk and Wagnalls, 1953), p. 161.
45. The New York Times, November 16, 1971.
46. Ibid.
47. Ibid.
48. Select Committee on Crime, *Hearings into Narcotics Research, Rehabilitation and Treatment,* U.S. House of Representatives, 92nd Cong., 1st sess., Serial 92-1, 1971, p. 3.
49. John F. Holahan, "The Economics of Heroin," in *Dealing with Drug Abuse, A Report to the Ford Foundation,* (New York: Praeger Publishers, 1972), pp. 278-279.
50. Ibid., p. 283.
51. The New York Times, November 16, 1971.
52. The New York Times, February 19, 1972.
53. New York Post, March 20, 1972.
54. Taped interview with New York Police Dept. narcotics officers, November 2, 1971.
55. Paul J. Curran, *New York Law Journal,* December 6, 1971, p. 38.
56. Cf. Chapter II.
57. The New York Times, February 4, 1972.
58. Ibid.
59. Herbert L. Packer, *The Limits of the Criminal Sanction,* (Palo Alto: Stanford U. Press, 1968), p. 332-33.
60. Lawrence Kolb, *Drug Addiction: A Medical Problem,* (Springfield: Charles C. Thomas, 1962), p. 172.

The British Experience

1. Dr. Granville W. Larimore and Dr. Henry Brill, "Report to Governor Nelson A. Rockefeller of an On the Site Study of the British Narcotic System" (mimeographed: March 3, 1959).
2. Bureau of Narcotics, U.S. Treasury Department, *Narcotic Clinics in the United States,* (Washington, D.C.: U.S. Government Printing Office, 1953).
3. Ibid.
4. *Annual Report* of the Commissioner of Internal Revenue for the Fiscal Year ended June 30, 1919, (Washington, D.C.: U.S. Government Printing Office), p. 61.
5. Ibid., for 1920, p. 34.

6. Alfred R. Lindesmith, *The Addict and the Law,* (New York: Vintage Books, 1965), p. 141.
7. Charles Terry and Mildren Pellens, *The Opium Problem,* (Bureau of Social Hygiene, 1928), pp. 864-872.
8. *Narcotics Clinics in the United States,* op. cit., pp. 12-13.
9. Terry and Pellens, op. cit., p. 31.
10. Ibid., p. 40.
11. Ibid., p. 870.
12. The man who did this most fully, Alfred Lindesmith, was the object of Bureau harassment. Cf. *The Addict and the Law,* op. cit., p. 254-257.
13. *Treatment and Rehabilitation of Narcotic Addicts:* Report of the Committee on the Judiciary, U.S. Senate, containing the Findings and Recommendations of the Subcommittee on Improvements in the Federal Criminal Code pursuant to S. Res. 67 and S. Res. 166, 84th Cong., 2nd sess., S. Rep. No. 1850 (Washington, D.C.: U.S. Government Printing Office, 1956), p. 3-12.
14. Vera Institute of Justice, Inc., *Heroin Research and Rehabilitation Program,* Discussion Proposal, May, 1971, (mimeograph).
15. Journal of the American Medical Association, 156, No. 8 (October 23, 1954), p. 788.
16. Cited in Lindesmith, op. cit., p. 173.
17. Edwin M. Schur, *Narcotic Addiction in Britain and America: The Import of Public Policy.* (Bloomington: Indiana University Press, 1962), p. 76.
18. Lindesmith, op. cit., p. 176.
19. Henry Brill and Granville W. Larimore, "An Analysis: How Britain Handles Its Drug Problem," *New York Law Journal,* December 6, 1971, p. 37.
20. Ibid.
21. Ibid.
22. Ibid.
23. Edgar May, "Narcotics Addiction and Control in Great Britain" in *Dealing with Drug Abuse,* A Report to the Ford Foundation, (New York: Praeger Publishers, 1972), p. 353.
24. Ibid., p. 352.
25. Ibid., p. 351.
26. Ibid., p. 349.
27. Vera Institute of Justice, op. cit.
28. Vera Institute of Justice, op. cit.
29. Edgar May, op. cit., p. 354.
30. Vera Institute of Justice, Inc., Staff paper, 1971.
31. Henry Brill and Granville W. Larimore, op. cit., p. 37.
32. Edgar May, op. cit., p. 349.
33. Ibid., p. 389.
34. Ibid., p. 371.
35. Ibid., p. 378.
36. Vera Institute of Justice Inc., Staff Paper, 1971.
37. Ibid.
38. Quoted in Lindesmith, op. cit., p. 187.
39. See Lindesmith, op. cit., p. 176., and Brill and Larimore, op. cit., p. 37.

40. Lady Frankau, "Treatment in England of Canadian Patients Addicted to Narcotic Drugs." The Canadian Medical Association Journal, 90, No. 6 (February 8, 1964), 421-4.
41. Ibid., p. 422.
42. Edgar May, op. cit., p. 390-91.
43. Ibid., p. 391.
44. New York Times, February 4, 1972.

Civil Commitment, Methadone, and Other Follies

1. Charles Terry and Mildred Pellens, The Opium Problem, (Bureau of Social Hygiene, 1928), p. 627.
2. The New York Times, April 10, 1972.
3. Ibid.
4. New York Post, January 8, 1972.
5. Vincent P. Dole, "Research on Methadone Maintenance Treatment," The International Journal of the Addictions, 5 (3), September, 1970, p. 363.
6. The New York Times, May 18, 1972.
7. James V. DeLong, "Treatment and Rehabilitation," in Dealing with Drug Abuse, A Report to the Ford Foundation, (New York: Praeger Publishers, 1972), p. 202.
8. The New York Times, April 10, 1972.
9. James V. Delong, op. cit., p. 191.
10. Ibid., p. 194-195.
11. The New York Times, March 22, 1970.
12. Ibid.
13. Health Policy Advisory Center, Health/PAC Bulletin, June, 1970, p. 20.
14. James V. DeLong, op. cit., p. 195.
15. Terry and Pellens, p. 825.
16. Ibid., p. 830.
17. Report of Reference Comm. on Legis. & Public Relations, 82, Journal of the American Medical Association, 1967 (1924).
18. John C. Kramer, "The State Versus the Addict: Uncivil Commitment," in 1 Drug Abuse Law Review (1971), p. 246.
19. Cited in James V. Delong, op. cit., p. 183.
20. John C. Kramer, op. cit., note 47, p. 246.
21. Bureau of Narcotics, U.S. Treasury Department, Narcotic Clinics in the United States (Washington D.C.: U.S. Government Printing Office, 1953), p. 23.
22. Alfred R. Lindesmith, The Addict and the Law, (New York: Vintage Books, 1965), p. 136-137.
23. Cited in John C. Kramer, op. cit., p. 249.
24. Troy Duster, The Legislation of Morality (New York: Free Press, 1970), note 4, p. 134.
25. John C. Kramer, op. cit., p. 249.
26. Health Policy Advisory Center, op. cit., p. 16-17.
27. Cited in John C. Kramer, op. cit., p. 248.
28. The New York Times, March 27, 1967.

29. John C. Kramer, op. cit., p. 248.
30. Ibid., p. 258.
31. James V. DeLong, op. cit., p. 186.
32. John C. Kramer, op. cit., p. 256.
33. Ibid., p. 258.
34. Ibid., p. 251.
35. Ibid., p. 252.
36. James V. DeLong, op. cit., p. 187.
37. Ibid.
38. Powell v. Texas, 392 U.S. 514 (1968), p. 529.
39. Robinson v. California, 370 U.S. 660 (1962), p. 665.
40. Herman Joseph and Vincent P. Dole, M.D., "Methadone Patients on
    Probation and Parole," *Federal Probation,* June, 1970, Unpaged re-
    print.
41. Ibid.
42. Ibid.
43. F.R. Gearing, "Evaluation of Methadone Maintenance Treatment for
    Heroin Addiction: A Progress Report." Paper paresented at the Third
    National Conference on Methadone Treatment, New York, November,
    1970.
44. James V. DeLong, op. cit., p. 207.
45. Ibid.
46. F.R. Gearing, "Successes and Failures in Methadone Treatment of Heroin
    Addiction in New York City." Paper presented at the Third National
    Conference on Methadone Treatment. New York, November, 1970.
47. Ibid.
48. Herman Joseph and Vincent Dole, op. cit.
49. James V. DeLong, op. cit., p. 203.
50. Health Policy Advisory Center, op. cit., p. 17.
51. Ibid.
52. Ibid.
53. Edgar May, "Narcotics Addiction and Control in Great Britain," in
    Dealing with Drug Abuse, A Report to the Ford Foundation, (New
    York: Praeger Publishers, 1972) and Vera Institute of Justice Inc.,
    Staff paper, 1971.
54. O. Lee McCabe, "Methadone Maintenance: Boon or Bane?" *The Drug
    Abuse Controversy,* (eds.), C.C. Brown and C. Savage, (Baltimore:
    National Educational Consultants, Inc., 1971), p. 129.
55. Ibid.
56. The New York Times, November 9, 1970.
57. Herman Joseph and Vincent P. Dole, op. cit.
58. O. Lee McCabe, op. cit., p. 128.
59. James V. DeLong, op. cit., p. 204.
60. Department of Health, The City of New York, *Narcotics Register Statis-
    tical Report*—1969, Table II.
61. Beth Israel Medical Center, *Methadone Maintenance Treatment Program,*
    pamphlet.
62. O. Lee McCabe, op. cit., p. 127.
63. W.F. Wieland, "Use of Phenothiazines and Antidepressants in the Treat-

ment of Depression and Schizophrenia in Methadone-Maintained Patients." Paper presented at the Third National Conference on Methadone Treatment, New York, November, 1970.

64. Herman Joseph and Vincent P. Dole, op. cit.
65. New York Post, February 28, 1972.
66. James V. DeLong, op. cit., p. 227.
67. The New York Times, January 2, 1972.
68. Ibid.
69. Conversation with former addict, now working to rehabilitate addicts through political action. November, 1971.
70. James V. DeLong, op. cit., p. 223.
71. D.P. Ausubel, "The Dole-Nyswander Treatment of Heroin Addiction," *Journal of the American Medical Association,* No. 195, 1966, p. 165-166.
72. V.P. Dole and M.E. Nyswander, "The Use of Methadone for Narcotic Blockade," *British Journal of Addiction,* No. 63, 1968, pp. 55-57.
73. Marie E. Nyswander, "The Methadone Treatment of Heroin Addiction," *Hospital Practice,* Vol. 2, No. 4, April, 1967.
74. Edgar May, op. cit., p. 387 and Vera Institute of Justice Inc., Staff paper, 1971, p. 2.
75. May, op. cit., pp. 386-391, and Vera, op. cit., p. 11.

The Search for a Solution

1. Rufus King, 62 Yale Law Journal, 736-749, 1953.
2. Preliminary data from Narcotics Register given by Staff member, Flora Brophy, May, 1972.
3. The New York Times, May 18, 1972.
4. Edgar May, "Addiction and Control in Great Britain," in *Dealing with Drug Abuse, A Report to the Ford Foundation,* (New York: Praeger Publishers, 1972), p. 365.
5. James V. DeLong, "Treatment and Rehabilitation," in *Dealing with Drug Abuse, A Report to the Ford Foundation,* (New York: Praeger Publishers, 1972), p. 233.
6. William R. Martin, "National Institute's Search for Narcotics Antagonist," *New York Law Journal,* December 6, 1971, p. 34.
7. Ibid.
8. Ibid.
9. Ibid.
10. Ibid.
11. Ibid.
12. Ibid.
13. Albert A. LaVerne, from the tape recorded address given at Hahnemann Medical College and Hospital, Philadelphia, February 2, 1972.
14. Ibid.
15. Ibid.
16. Albert A. LaVerne and Morris Herman, "An Evaluation of Carbon Dioxide Therapy," *The American Journal of Psychiatry,* Vol. 112, No. 2, August, 1955, p. 111.

17. Ibid., p. 109.
18. Ibid., p. 112.
19. LaVerne, op. cit.
20. Ibid.
21. Lewis C. Mills, from tape recorded address given at Hahnemann Medical College and Hospital, Philadelphia, February 2, 1972.
22. Ibid.
23. Lewis C. Mills, Telephone conversation, May 30, 1972.
24. William James, *The Varieties of Religious Experience,* (New York: Longmans, Green, 1902).
25. Abram Hoffer, "Treatment of Alcoholism with Psychedelic Therapy," *Psychedelics,* B. Aaronson and H. Osmond (eds.), (Garden City: Anchor Books, 1970).
26. W.N. Pahnke, A.A. Kurland, S. Unger, C. Savage, and S. Graf, "The Experimental Use of Psychedelic (LSD) Psychotherapy," *Journal of the American Medical Association,* No. 212, 1970. pp. 1856-1863.
27. Abram Hoffer, op. cit., p. 361.
28. Charles Savage and O. Lee McCabe, "Psychedelic (LSD) Therapy of Drug Addiction," *The Drug Abuse Controversy,* (eds.) C.C. Brown and C. Savage, (Baltimore: National Educational Consultants Inc., 1972), p. 152.
29. Vera Institute of Justice Inc., *Heroin Research and Rehabilitation Program: Discussion Proposal,* May, 1971.
30. The New York Times, February 4, 1972.
31. Vera, op. cit.
32. Ibid.
33. The New York Times, May 11, 1972.
34. Vera, op. cit.
35. See Charles E. Terry, "Narcotic Drug Addiction and Rational Administration," *American Medicine,* 26 (January, 1920), p. 29.

BIBLIOGRAPHY

Abramson, H., *The Use of LSD in Psychotherapy and Alcoholism*. Indianapolis: The Bobbs-Merrill Co., Inc., 1967.

Adams, Nina S. and Alfred W. McCoy (eds.), *Laos: War and Revolution*. New York: Harper, 1970.

American Bar Association and the American Joint Committee on Narcotic Drugs, *Drug Addiction: Crime or Disease?* Bloomington: Indiana University Press, 1963.

Anslinger, Harry J. and Will Oursler, *The Murderers! The Shocking Story of the Narcotics Gangs*. New York: Farrar, Straus and Cudahy, 1961.

Anslinger, Harry J. and William F. Tompkins. *The Traffic in Narcotics*. New York: Funk and Wagnalls, 1953.

Ball, J. and C. Chambers (eds.), *The Epidemiology of Opiate Addiction in the United States*. Springfield, Ill.: Charles C. Thomas, 1970.

Barber, Bernard, *Drugs and Society*. New York: Russell Sage Foundation, 1967.

Bonnie, R.S. and C.H. Whitebread, II, "The Forbidden Fruit and the Tree of Knowledge: An Inquiry into the Legal History of American Marijuana Prohibition," *Virginia Law Review*, Vol. 56, No. 6, October, 1970.

Brown, Clinton C. and Charles Savage, (eds.), *The Drug Abuse Controversy*. Baltimore: National Educational Consultants, Inc., 1971.

Browning, Frank and Banning Garrett, "The New Opium War," *Ramparts*. May, 1971.

Bureau of Narcotics, U.S. Treasury Department, *Narcotic Clinics in the United States*. Washington, D.C.: U.S. Government Printing Office, 1953.

   Prescribing and Dispensing of Narcotics Under the Harrison Narcotic Law. Pamphlet No. 56, Revised: September, 1960.

Burroughs, W., *Junkie*. New York: Ace Books, Inc., 1953.

Chein, I., D. Gerard, R. Lee, and E. Rosenfeld, *The Road to H.* New York: Basic Books, 1964.

Collis, Morris, *Foreign Mud.* New York: Knopf, 1947.

De Ropp, R.S., *Drugs and the Mind.* New York: Grove Press, Evergreen Black Cat Edition, 1957.

Joseph, H., and V.P. Dole, "Methadone Patients on Probation and Parole," *Federal Probation.* June, 1970.

Eldridge, W.B., *Narcotics and the Law: A Critique of the American Experiment in Narcotic Drug Control.* American Bar Foundation, 1962.

The Ford Foundation, *Dealing with Drug Abuse: A Report to the Ford Foundation.* New York: Praeger Publishers, 1972.

Fort, Joel, *The Pleasure Seekers: The Drug Crisis, Youth and Society.* New York: Grove Press, Inc., Evergreen Black Cat Edition, 1970.

"Giver of Delight or Liberator of Sin: Drug Use and 'Addiction' in Asia," U.N. *Bulletin on Narcotics,* Vol. 17, 3 and 4, 1965.

Goldstein, A., L. Aronow, and S. Kalman, *Principles of Drug Action.* New York: Harper and Row, 1968.

Goodman, L., and A. Gilman, *The Pharmacological Basis of Therapeutics.* (4th ed.), New York: Macmillan, 1970.

Harris, Richard, *Justice.* New York: Dutton, 1969.

Health Policy Advisory Council, Health/Pac *Bulletin.* June, 1970.

Hentoff, Nat, *A Doctor Among the Addicts.* New York: Grove Press Inc., Evergreen Black Cat Edition, 1970.

James, William, *The Varieties of Religious Experience.* New York: Longmaus, Green, 1902.

Kamm, Henry, "Asians Doubt that U.S. Can Halt Heroin Flow," *New York Times.* August 11, 1971.

King, Rufus, *The Drug Hang-Up—America's Fifty Year Trip.* New York: W.W. Norton, 1972.

Kolb, Lawrence, *Drug Addiction: A Medical Problem.* Springfield, Ill.: Charles C. Thomas, 1962.

Larner, J. and R. Tefferteller, *The Addict in the Street*. Zebra Books, 1966.

Laurie, P., *Drugs*. Baltimore: Penguin Books Inc., 1967.

Lewin, L., *Phantastica: Narcotic and Stimulant Drugs*. New York: E.P. Dutton & Co., Inc., 1964.

Light, Arthur and Edward Torrance, *Opium Addiction*. New York: Archives of Internal Medicine, 1929.

Lingeman, R.R., *Drugs from A to Z: A Dictionary*. New York: McGraw-Hill Book Company, 1969.

Lindesmith, Alfred R., *The Addict and the Law*. New York: Vintage Books, 1967.

Malcolm X, *The Autobiography of Malcolm X*. New York: Grove Press, Inc., 1966.

McAlister, J.T., *Vietnam: The Origin of Revolution*. New York: Alfred A. Knopf, 1969.

McCoy, A., *The Politics of Heroin in South East Asia*. New York: Harper and Row, 1972.

The Non-Medical Use of Drugs. Interim Report of the Canadian Government's Commission of Inquiry. Baltimore: Penguin Books Inc., 1971.

Nyswander, M., *The Drug Addict as a Patient*. New York: Grune and Stratton, 1956.

    "The Methadone Treatment of Heroin Addiction," *Hospital Practice*. April, 1967.

Owen, David Edward, *British Opium Policy in China and India*. "Yale Historical Studies," Vol. VIII. New Haven: Yale University Press, 1934.

Roueche, Berton, *The Neutral Spirit: A Portrait of Alcohol*. New York: Little, Brown & Co., 1960.

Schur, E.M., *Crimes Without Victims*. Prentice-Hall, Inc., 1965.

    Narcotic Addiction in Britain and America: The Import of Public Policy. Bloomington: Indiana University Press, 1962.

Scott, Peter Dale, "Heroin Traffic: Some Amazing Coincidences," *Earth*. March, 1972.

Sinclair, A., *Prohibition: The Era of Excess.* Boston: Little, Brown & Co., 1962.

Terry, Charles and Mildren Pellens, *The Opium Problem.* Bureau of Social Hygiene, 1928.

Terry, Charles E., "Narcotic Drug Addiction and Rational Administration," *American Medicine,* 26. January, 1920.

Tara, Santi, "Southeast Asia: Super Supplier of Heroin," *World,* Vol. 1, No. 1, July 4, 1972.

Thayer, George, *The War Business.* New York: Simon and Schuster, 1969.

Thomas, Piri, *Down These Mean Streets.* New York: Alfred A. Knopf, Inc., 1967.

Trocchi, Alexander, *Cain's Book.* New York, Grove Press, 1960.

Ungerleider, J.T. (ed.), *The Problems and Prospects of LSD.* Springfield, Ill.: Charles C. Thomas, 1968.

Volk, Lester D., *Narcotic Drug Addiction: Speech of Hon. Lester D. Volk of New York in the House of Representatives, Friday, January 13, 1922.* Washington, D.C.: U.S. Government Printing Office, 1922.

Wakefield, Dan (ed.), *The Addict.* Greenwich: Fawcett Publications Inc., 1963.

Wikler, A. (ed.), *The Addictive States.* Baltimore: Williams and Wilkins, Inc., 1968.

   Opiate Addiction. Springfield, Ill.: Charles C. Thomas, 1953.

Yablonsky, L., *Synanon: The Tunnel Back.* Baltimore: Penguin Books Inc., 1967.

INDEX

Air America, 15

Addiction. *See* Narcotics addiction

Addiction Research Center, 209

Addiction Research Unit (U.K.), 162, 165

Addiction Services Agency (N.Y.C.), 45

Addicts. *See* Heroin addicts

Alcohol, 112, 115, 193, 222

Alcoholics Anonymous, 215

Alcoholism, x, 59, 213, 215, 216, 232

Algren, Nelson, 60

Ambrose, Myles J., x, 43, 44, 48, 133

American Bar Association, 127; Report of, 127-28

American Medical Association, 124, 127, 177; Report of, 127-28

Amphetamines, 193, 194

Analgesics, 227

Anslinger, Harry, 10, 41, 60, 66-67, 127, 128, 129, 130, 178

Antagonists. *See* Chemical antagonists

Baden, Michael, 46, 47

Barbiturates, x, 112, 113, 193, 194

Bayer Company, 6

Bergner, Lawrence, 46, 47

Bill of Rights, 109

Bishop, Ernest S., 126, 127

Bloomquist, Edward R., 68, 69

Blue Laws, 109

Boggs Bill (U.S., 1951), 125. *See also* Federal laws

Boylan, John, 176

Boylan Law (N.Y., 1914), 176

Brain Committee (U.K.), 153; Report, 160

Brill, Henry, 150, 151, 152, 156, 163

British system. *See* Narcotics addiction, treatment in England

Brixton Prison, 158

Brookdale Hospital Center, 193

Brown, L.P., 50

Buckley, John J., 167

Bureau of Narcotics, 39, 55, 144-45, 146, 147, 151, 178-79. *See also* Bureau of Narcotics and Dangerous Drugs

Bureau of Narcotics and Dangerous Drugs (BNDD), 11, 16, 84, 111, 114, 132, 144, 149, 158, 163; estimates of addicts by, x, 24, 39, 40-41, 43-44, 48

Canadian drug laws, 164-65

Carbon dioxide therapy (CDT), 208, 211-15, 232-43; danger in, 239-40; effectiveness of, 240-43

Central Intelligence Agency (CIA), 12, 13, 15

Chemical antagonists, 208-11

Chia Ch'ing, Emperor, 4

Chien, Isador, 62

China, Nationalist, 10
China, People's Republic of, 10, 11
Cigarettes, 113
Civil commitment programs, 170, 176-85, 201, 204; costs of, 191; philosophy of, 178-79. *See also* Heroin addicts, treatment programs for
Clinics. *See* Narcotics clinics
Cocaine, 115, 153
Commission on Narcotic Drugs, U.N., 11
Committee on Narcotic Drugs (AMA), 124
Comprehensive Drug Abuse Prevention & Control Act (U.S., 1970), 125. *See also* Federal laws
Corruption. *See* Police corruption
Cyclazocine, 208

Dangerous Drug Laws (U.K., 1920), 150-51
Dangerous Drugs Act (U.K., 1967), 153
Daniel Committee, 67
Davis, Miryam, 195, 196
Daytop, 172, 175
Dealing with Drug Abuse, 48, 176
DeLong, James V., 176
DeMott, Benjamin, 128
Diacetylmorphine, 227. *See also* Heroin
Dimock, Edward J., 128
Dole, Vincent, 72, 73, 186, 187, 188, 190, 192, 193, 195, 198, 199, 200

Dolophine, 186. *See also* Methadone
Drug Abuse Controversy, The (ed. Brown & Savage), 217
Drug Addiction: Crime or Disease?, 128
Drug addiction. *See* Narcotics addiction; Heroin addiction
Drug education, 221
Drugs, 29, 30
Drugs from A to Z: A Dictionary, 29
DuMez, A.G., 38-39
Durk, David, 139

Earle, C.H., 50
English East India Company, 4
Erasistratus, 3
Euphoriants, 227

Fact Sheets, 40
Federal Bureau of Narcotics, Advisory Committee to, 127, 128, 129. *See also* Bureau of Narcotics
"Federal Law and Drug Addiction," (Lindesmith), 117
Federal laws: and drugs, 116-26, 129-35, 139, 141, 146, 148, 204. *See also* Harrison Narcotics Act; State laws
Feinberg, Samuel, 36
Forbes, 29
Fort, Joel, 14
Frankau, Lady, 164, 165

Gearing, Frances, 188, 192
Giordano, Henry, 41, 150
Glue-sniffing, 112

Gollance, Harvey, 192
Green Berets. *See* U.S. Special
    Forces
Greenwood, Joseph, 41, 42, 43,
    44, 46, 84

Harlem, 30
Harrison Narcotics Act (1914),
    6, 37, 49, 54, 56, 125, 145,
    146, 200; provisions of, 117,
    118; purpose of, 116-17, 150,
    226; interpretations of, 118-
    23, 127, 129, 144
Hartwell, B.H., 50
Hepatitis, 228-29
Herman, Morris, 212
Heroin:
    abstinence from, 170-71, 173,
    193; amount of U.S., 21-22,
    23, 31, 48-49; availability of,
    71, 131, 132-33, 135, 160,
    206-207, 223, 225; control
    of, 20, 22-23; craving for, 84-
    86, 188, 210; demand, 129;
    distribution process, 20-21,
    25-29, 134, 206, 221; H-4, 9;
    legalization of, 206-207, 221,
    222, 224-26; methods of
    using, 31-33; origins of U.S.,
    10-19, 22-23, 185; overdoses,
    28*n*, 41; pharmacology of, 2,
    62, 227, 229-31; physical de-
    pendence on, 84, 231; and
    police corruption, 136-39;
    prices of, 19-20, 24, 26, 30,
    131, 148, 160, 221; produc-
    tion, 6, 8-9, 19; profits in, 30-
    31, 206; "purity," 29; seizures,
    131, stabilization on, 200,
    223; tolerance of, 84, 231;

traffic, viii, ix, 21, 24, 131-
    33, 160-61; U.S. government
    involvement in, 12-13; U.S.
    history of, 6, 54-56, 163,
    198; Vietnam, 32, 246-47,
    249; withdrawal, 231, 244-
    45. *See also* Heroin addicts
Heroin addiction, 36-38, 45,
    198; "cures," 171, 207-208,
    214-15, 220-21; difference
    between methadone and, 199-
    200; important factors in, 84-
    86; law enforcement policy
    regarding, 130-31, 133-36,
    139, 157, 176-85, 197-98,
    201, 204-206, 226; process
    of, 61-63, 75-80; theories of,
    63-73, 188, 200, 220, 230;
    U.S. treatment programs for,
    See Heroin addicts, treatment
    programs for. *See also*
    Heroin; Heroin addicts
Heroin addicts: average age of,
    39, 47, 50, 52, 206; black,
    56, 58, 164; Canadian, 164-
    66; and class, 50-51, 55; and
    crime, 53, 54, 113, 136, 172-
    73, 190, 193, 197, 201, 204,
    206-207, 221, 225, 226;
    "curing," 171, 207-208, 214-
    15, 220-21; differences
    between methadone and,
    199-200; employment of,
    173, 190, 192, 225; in
    England, 97, 98, 100-103,
    149-60, 162, 165, 167-68,
    192, 207, 229; estimating
    number of U.S., ix, 5, 24, 36-
    48, 49, 135; female, 58; incar-
    ceration of, 176-77, 180, 182-

83; I.Q.s, 72, 73; location of U.S., 47-48; male, 58, 164; myths about, 58-72, 111; personal characteristics of, 73; physical damage to, 113, 228; profiles of New York City, 52-54, 74; treatment programs for, 170-201, 208-220, 232-43, 244, 250; in Vietnam, vii, 9, 244, 246-52; white, 56, 58. *See also* Heroin; Heroin addiction

Heroin dealers, 19-21, 26-28, 30, 31, 55, 56, 60-61, 130, 133, 134, 135; English, 98-100; major, 132-34

Heroin maintenance clinics, 129, 223-24

Heroin users, 84, 85-86; ages of, 52; attitudes toward, 110-11; myths about, 60-64, 84, 113; number of, 24-25, 49, 135; physical damage to, 112-13; profiles of, 52-54, 74-81, 87-105; in Vietnam, 9, 10

Hoffer, Abram, 215, 216

Holahan, John F., 37, 48

Hudson Institute, 48

Hull, J.M., 50

Ingersoll, John E., 11, 41

Insidious Dr. Fu-Manchu, The (Rohmer), 115

International Narcotic Education Association, 38

International Narcotics Control Board, U.N., 8, 16

International Opium Convention (1912), 116

Iran, 18

Irwin, Samuel, 112

Jaffey, Jerome, 249

James, William, 215

Jim Fuey Moy v. U.S., 118

Joint Committee of the A.B.A. and the A.M.A. on Narcotic Drugs (1958), 127-28

Joseph, Herman, 190

"Junk," 6

Justice Department, 43, 133

Khiem, Tran van, 13

King, Rufus, 124, 204

Knapp Commission, 139

Kolb, Lawrence, 38-39, 58, 59, 141

Kramer, John C., 177, 178

Ky, Nguyen cao, 13

Larimore, Granville, 150, 151, 152

Laudanum, 5. *See also* Opium

LaVerne, Albert A., 211-13, 214, 215, 232

Law. *See* Federal laws; State laws

Ledain Commission (Canada), 111, 112

Limits of Criminal Sanction, The (Packer), 139

Linder, Dr., 121, 122, 123, 124, 125

Lindesmith, Alfred, 39, 116, 117, 120, 151, 163

Lingeman, R.L., 29

Lister, Joseph, 115

LSD, ix, 2, 113

LSD therapy, 208, 215-20, 236-37

McCabe, O. Lee, 217, 218, 219, 220
McCarthy, Joseph, 114
Madden, William H., 179
Mafia. *See* Organized crime
"Mainlining," 32
Man with the Golden Arm, The (Algren), 60
Marijuana, viii, ix, 110, 129; and heroin, 66-71, 113, 140
Marijuana Tax Act (U.S., 1937), 66
Marshall, O., 39
May, Edgar, 158, 165
Meduna, L.J., 211, 212, 234
Methadone, 97, 102, 154, 185, 210; and heroin, 186, 199-200; babies, 195-96; detoxification, 187
Methadone addiction: and crime, 190, 193, 197, 204, 206-207, 221; in England, 154-56, 158, 168; medical problems of, 170, 195-96, 242; moral objections to, 196-98; social problems of, 196-97
Methadone Maintenance Evaluation Unit, 188-90, 192-93
Methadone maintenance programs, 46, 170, 172-73, 185-95, 201, 205, 206, 224; costs of, 191, in England, 200; social problems of, 194, 196-97, 210-11. *See also* Heroin addicts, treatment programs for
Methamphetamine, 112
Mexico, 8
Mills, Lewis, 213, 214
Milman, Doris, 68

Morphine, 12, 118, 185, 227, 228; effects of, 229-31; history of use of, 5-6, 51, 54, 55, 148; prices of, 148; properties of, 19, 62, 63, 96
Murphy, Morgan, 9
Murphy, Patrick, V., 36, 166, 223

Naloxone, 208-209
Narcotic antagonists, 224
Narcotic Clinics in the United States, 144, 147, 178
Narcotics (Williams), 10
Narcotics addiction: and federal laws, 117-22, 126-27, 130, 134-36, 140-41, 144, 146, 148; and state laws, 108-11, 113, 140-41, 176-77, 180-81; attitudes toward, 124; failure of policies regarding, 204-207, 226; growth rate of, 221, 222; medical approach to, 124, 126-27, 144, 167; -related crime, 161, 162, 166-67, 172-73, 193, 201, 222; treatment in England, 149-68, 192; treatment in U.S., *See* Heroin addicts, treatment programs for. *See also* Heroin addiction; Methadone addiction; Opiate addiction; Federal laws; State laws
Narcotics Addiction Control Commission (New York), 181, 184
Narcotics clinics, 144-49; attitudes toward, 148-49; in England, 155-57, 158-59, 161, 167, 192-93, 200, 223-25; New Haven, 148; New

York City, 149, 223; proposals for U.S., 166-67, 179, 223

Narcotics Drug Control Act (U.S., 1956), 125. *See also* Federal laws

Narcotics hospital (Lexington, Kentucky), 177

Narcotics Register (New York City), 44-47, 49, 51, 53, 74, 135, 194

Narcotics Treatment Administration (D.C.), 193, 195

Narcotics treatment programs. *See* Heroin addicts, treatment programs for; Civil commitment programs; Methadone maintenance programs; Therapeutic communities

Narcotics treatment techniques. *See* Carbon dioxide therapy; Chemical antagonists; LSD therapy

Narcotics use, 49-54, 221-23

National Institute of Mental Health, 216

Nationalist Chinese Army, 10, 12

Nepenthe, 2. *See also* Opium

New York Academy of Medicine, 179

New York City Addiction Services Agency. *See* Addiction Services Agency

New York City Health Code, 45

New York City Narcotics Register. *See* Narcotics Register

New York City Police Department, 62, 131, 135, 138;

Narcotics Bureau, 24, 29

New York Times, 17, 29, 136, 139, 167, 178, 196, 244, 252

Nixon, Richard, 130, 133, 134

Nyswander, Marie, 64, 65, 73, 85, 186, 198, 199, 200

Odyssey House, 172, 175

Office for Drug Abuse Law Enforcement, 43

Olivieri, Antonio G., 223

Operation Intercept, viii

Opiate addiction, 59, 111, 184, 208; attitudes toward, 124; as disease, 124; and state laws, 110-11; myths about, 112-15

Opiate addict-users, 207; attitudes toward, 111-15, 124; and crime, 113, 225; physical damage in, 112; and work, 113, 225

Opium, 7, 9, 16-19, 227, 246; history of use of, 3-5, 37, 39, 49-51, 54, 55, 114-15, 207; physical effects of, 2, 3, 228-30; production, 7-8, 16-19

Opium Problem, The (Terry and Pellens), 37, 126, 147

Opium Wars, 4

Organized crime; and heroin, 15, 20, 22-23, 28, 140

Osmond, Humphry, 215

Packer, Herbert, 139

Paracelsus, 5

Patrick, Sherman, 46, 47

Pellens, Mildred, 37, 38, 49, 113, 147, 148, 171, 200, 225

Phoenix House, 172, 175
Ploscowe, Morris, 127
Police corruption, 136-39
Powell v. Texas, 185
President's Commission on Law Enforcement and the Administration of Justice (1967), 63, 67
Prohibition Bureau's Regulations, 123
Prostitution, 114, 182
Psychedelic therapy. See LSD therapy
Psychedelic (LSD) Therapy of Narcotic Addiction (Savage & McCabe), 216

Rattikone, Ouane, 13
Respiratory depression, 229
Robinson v. California, 185
Rohmer, Sax, 115
Rolleston Committee (U.K.), 151; Report, 152
Rossides, Eugene T., 22, 131
Russell Sage Foundation, 128

Savage, Charles, 216, 218, 219, 220
Seymour, Whitney North Jr., 22, 131
Shreveport Clinic, 144, 147, 148. See also Narcotics clinics
"Skin-popping," 32
"Smoking," 31
"Snorting," 32
South America, 23
Southeast Asia, 8, 11, 22, 23
State laws: and addicts, 176-77, 180-85, 204; and drugs, 108-11, 113, 125, 139, 140, 141.

See also Federal laws
Steele, Robert, 9
Supreme Court decisions: on drugs, 118-19, 122, 146, 185; effects of, 120-21, 122. See also Federal laws
Synanon, 175, 246

Talese, Gay, 20
Terry, Charles, 37, 38, 49, 50, 113, 125, 126, 147, 148, 171, 200, 225
Thailand, 12
Therapeutic communities, 170, 208, 215, 224; costs of, 191; treatment methods of, 173-76, 201. See also Heroin addicts, treatment programs for
Thieu, Nguyen van, 13
Thorazine, 247
Tolerance, 230
Tranquilizers, x
Treasury Department, 119, 120, 123, 124, 147, 151
Treatment programs. See Civil commitment programs; Methadone maintenance programs; Therapeutic communities
Treatment techniques. See Carbon dioxide therapy; Chemical antagonists; LSD therapy
Tripp, Margaret, 154, 162
Turkey, 8, 11, 12, 16-19, 23

United Nations Commission on Narcotic Drugs, 11
United Nations International

Narcotics Control Board, 8

U.S. Army: heroin use in, vii, 9-10, 246-52

U.S. Congress, 43

U.S. Constitution, 109

U.S. Government: involvement in heroin, 12-15

U.S. News and World Report, 43

U.S. Special Forces, 12

U.S. v. Anthony, 122

U.S. v. Behrman, 119, 122

U.S. v. Jim Fuey Moy, 118

Vera Institute of Justice, 155, 168, 223, 224

Vietnam, 32, 246-47, 249

Volk, Lester D., 119, 120, 126, 127

Volk-Metcalfe Bill (N.Y.), 181

Volstead Act, 109, 146

Webb v. U.S., 118, 122, 125

Whitney Law (New York, 1917), 177

Williams, John B., 10

Winick, Charles, 111

Winter Soldier Hearings, 15

Yolles, Seymour, 209

Yung Cheng, Emperor, 3